D1106198

RELIGIOUS ASPECTS OF HYPNOSIS

RELIGIOUS ASPECTS OF HYPNOSIS

By

WILLIAM J. BRYAN, JR., M.D.

Fellow, Past President and Executive Director
The American Institute of Hypnosis
Los Angeles, California

With Forewords by

S. J. VAN PELT, M.B., B.S.
President of the British Society of Medical Hypnotists
London, England

and

REV. H. R. BURNETT
Pastor, First Foursquare Church
Compton, California

CHARLES C THOMAS • PUBLISHER
Springfield • Illinois • U.S.A.

CHARLES C THOMAS • PUBLISHER
BANNERSTONE HOUSE
301-327 East Lawrence Avenue, Springfield, Illinois, U.S.A.

With *THOMAS BOOKS* careful attention is given to all details of manufacturing and design. It is the Publisher's desire to present books that are satisfactory as to their physical qualities and artistic possibilities and appropriate for their particular use. THOMAS BOOKS will be true to those laws of quality that assure a good name and good will.

Printed in the United States of America

FOREWORD

As President of the British Society of Medical Hypnotists, and Editor of the British Journal of Medical Hypnotism, I am naturally concerned with the future of hypnotism.

In my first book, "Hypnotism and the Power Within," first published in 1950, my opening sentence in the preface stated: "This book has been written to show that hypnotism is a rational Christian procedure . . . ," and I suggested in the opening chapter that hypnotism was the **Method** by which the Divine Will was executed in many of the miracles of Christ. It, therefore, gives me great pleasure that Dr. William J. Bryan, Jr. has devoted a whole book to the religious aspects of hypnosis.

Having lectured for the American Institute of Hypnosis, of which Dr. Bryan is the President, in courses for medical men held as far apart as Paris (France), Hawaii and the West Indies, I have had ample opportunity to observe Dr. Bryan's outstanding teaching ability.

In my opinion this book will fill a very real need, and is a "must" not only for medical hypnotists who wish to use religious principles in their treatment, but also for clergymen He gives clearly the views on hypnosis held by the various who wish to understand the scientific reasons behind the success of their ministrations, and for all those who wish to extend their sphere of influence for the good of mankind.

Dr. Bryan deals with the subject in the fullest possible manner, and a wealth of research must have gone into the production of this book. Among a host of other important things, Dr. Bryan shows us how hypnotic techniques can bind us to religion, and how prayer is akin to a state of hypnosis.

He gives clearly the views on hypnosis held by the various faiths, Catholic, Jewish, Protestant, and others, including those of the Far East. He shows how hypnosis, like religion, is natural, powerful, and universal, and explains how the prophets produced visions by hypnosis. A special chapter is devoted to hypnosis and prayer, and a logical explanation is given of how prayers can change things.

Another chapter is devoted to examples of how Jesus used hypnosis to heal. Cases are quoted to illustrate the clinical use of religious principles in hypno-analysis in another chapter.

A further chapter is devoted to how hypnosis can help in the search for God, and a final chapter is devoted to the hypnotic proof of God.

Dr. Bryan has produced a truly great and original work in the realms of hypnosis and religion — all the greater because he has resisted the temptation which besets many authors, to be too dogmatic.

Dr. Bryan believes in practicing what he preaches, and although this work is of such excellence, he does in fact, as I have often heard him say in his inspiring lectures, "Leave something to God.'

S. J. VAN PELT, M.B., B.S.
Harley Street
London, W1, England

FOREWORD

As an average Minister, with an average education and an ordinary church, with the usual problems, I feel that I can speak with some authority as how the typical Minister feels about the subject of hypnosis.

My association and training on this subject, which was very limited, left me with the feeling that hypnosis was a strange, mystical, not understood power, which carried with it superstitions and fears, particularly of the unknown.

This appears to be the general misconception of hypnosis, and this apprehension appears to be in the religious realm as well as in secular fields.

If this fallacy had not existed, it would have been much easier for those pioneering this almost untouched science to have accomplished a great deal more in a shorter amount of time.

Dr. Bryan's book, dealing with Hypnosis and Religion, takes hypnosis away from the areas of fear and mysticism, and puts it on a clear logical and scientific plane. His book also explains the soul and spirit of man and his relationship to God in a way that gives each reader a clear idea of how to exert an effort toward his Creator. This is of great interest to the Minister and the layman as well who wants to live a fuller, better, and more useful life.

Because of the fact that man is soul and spirit, and many times cannot be treated successfully by physical therapy alone, there has been a need for a new approach to deal with man and his problems. The Physician and Minister need to look more closely at hypnosis as a means to reach into the soul and the mind of man, which in turn will benefit spiritual and

physical healing and will have a tendency to reconcile the
ministry of spiritual healing with physical healing, which will
cause the Minister and the Physician to compliment one another.

Rev. H. R. Burnett
Pastor, First Foursquare Church
Compton, Calif.

PREFACE

To my knowledge, this is the first book of its kind outlining religious aspects of hypnosis, the way in which religion utilizes hypnosis to achieve its end, and the way in which medical hypnotists may also utilize religious principles in the analytic treatment of their patients. This book is intended to be the forerunner of a series of books dealing with various aspects of hypnotism in the professional world. This particular volume was intended to be of service primarily to those members of the medical profession who utilize hypnosis in their practice, and also to those clergymen who may wish to understand the means by which they are achieving a good deal of their positive results. It is realized that even the use of the word "hypnosis" in certain areas may be detrimental to the reputations of both clergymen and physicians, but as the light of truth begins to shine on subjects which have formerly been considered occult and mystic, understanding comes even to the average man. Indeed, sometimes the average man has a better conception of reality as it exists than those of us in the professions. One reason for this is, primarily, that as our studies center around specializations in our fields, we continue to learn more and more about less and less. This leads us to the minute examination of the leaves but a misconception of the grandeur of the forest. It is this limitless grandeur of the forest, the grandeur of nature itself, and the glorification of God in the highest to which the purpose of this book is humbly dedicated.

As was stated before, this book is intended to be merely a forerunner of a series of books, the next of which to be published will be a volume entitled "The Legal Aspects of

Hypnosis," which should be of interest both to physicians, attorneys, and law enforcement officials. Indeed, educators, psychologists, and informed laymen should also benefit from reading this work. It will contain chapters on laws regulating the practice of hypnosis, previous court decisions on hypnosis, hypnosis in crime, and many other subjects. A special chapter on winning cases through hypnosis dealing with relaxation of the nervous witness, the use of hypnosis in retrograde amnesia, improving faulty memory through hypnosis, semantics, and the influencing of a jury by means of hypnotic techniques should be of great interest to the legal profession. A special chapter on law enforcement will cover the use of hypnosis in safety programs as well as the complex art of interrogation of criminals. Special chapters have been devoted to the use of hypnosis in penal institutions, as well as a complete case report on the analysis of a psycho-killer, which was completed only this year. A section of international law and hypnosis includes the interrogation of prisoners-of-war, the techniques of brain washing, and also Powerization, a relatively new technique of psychological warfare polished to glistening smoothness in the black chambers of some iron-curtain countries. The final chapter on mass hypnotism will cover its use by dictators, as well as politicians and presidential candidates in this country. Various case histories will be illustrated, and the problem of sexual offenses and hypnosis will be thoroughly covered.

Following this, a complete course in hypnosis step by step will be published in an effort to give those physicians who have taken courses in hypnosis a complete reference volume with which they may refresh their memories, and to prepare other physicians who have not taken individual courses in hypnosis for such a course.

Completely dissimilar to any other publication which has been previously printed, it will take the physician, dentist or psychologist step by step teaching him every phase of the use of hypnosis in his profession. It will not only illustrate methods by which the techniques of hypnosis are mastered, but will also adequately cover the indications for their use as well as their limitations.

Further books on clinical hypnosis for those who have mastered the various specialized techniques will cover each and every disease process both in medicine and surgery, in which hypnosis has found an application.

Finally, a book designed to elucidate clearly and effectively the complex art of hypno-analysis and psycho-synthesis will be presented for publication.

It is hoped that the reader will approach the subject of this particular volume with a spirit of reverence, as it was written with such a spirit and with the guidance of prayer.

The author owes a debt of gratitude to his secretary, Reeta Barton, and other typists who have done much of the physical labor connected with the book. Especially I wish to mention the work of Miss Patience W. Brown, who performed the laborious undertaking of proof reading and indexing which is invariably a thankless task. I express my appreciation to Mr. Payne Thomas, of Charles C Thomas, Publisher who offered advice and criticism regarding the layout of the book, its length and its organization. I also wish to thank my wife, Olga, without whose patient understanding at times this book could never have been written. It is no secret to any author who also engages in a busy medical practice that the only way a medical book can be written is at the expense of those precious few hours which he desires to spend with his family. This is the bitter-sweet life of a medical author and medical lecturer.

I would like to acknowledge and thank the members of the clergy who offered their suggestions for this book. They include members of all faiths too numerous to mention, except that I would like to mention the clerical proof-reading done by my brother-in-law, Reverend Ray Burnett, and the use of quotations by Reverend Ray Lindquist, Doctor of Divinity, and Chief Pastor of the Hollywood First Presbyterian Church.

I am especially grateful to Reverend Ray Burnett, the Pastor of the Compton Four Square Church, for his making available to me his own mammoth concordance and bible study library. It was through the cooperation of all of these aforementioned people and through the guidance of our Lord and Savior Jesus Christ that I was able to complete this volume in its present form.

                                        WILLIAM J. BRYAN, JR., M.D.

CONTENTS

RELIGIOUS ASPECTS OF HYPNOSIS

Chapter I

INTRODUCTION AND DEFINITION

PART 1. INTRODUCTION

If we are going to discuss the religious aspects of hypnosis, it would seem that we should first know something about religion and something about hypnosis. It has always been a source of amazement to me that there exists so great a number of theologians who discuss hypnosis without knowing the first principle about it; and so many hypnotists who discuss religion without having the slightest idea regarding the meaning of the term. Indeed, as I have stated many times elsewhere, and as many others have stated more eloquently than I, terms and words have no meaning. Words only contain meaning as we attribute meaning to them. Words are, indeed, only so many letters put together; so many straight and curved lines appearing on a page, that have no meaning until someone gives us an idea in our mind, at which time we attribute a certain meaning to them. We are only able to communicate between one another because the meaning which I attribute to a word and the meaning which you attribute to a word have certain similarities. It should follow, therefore, that it is always impossible to completely communicate any idea from one mind to another through the use of words, because words never have the same meaning for any two people; nor do they ever completely describe any given idea or situation.

Nevertheless, in order to have a starting place, our attempt at communication must be firmly grounded in terms which we understand to the best of our ability. The dictionary defines religion as a belief in a divine or superhuman power or powers to be obeyed and worshipped as the creator and ruler of the universe. It also defines religion as the expression

3

of this belief, in conduct and virtue. Furthermore, it is described as a specific system of belief, worship and conduct often involving a code of ethics and philosophy, such as the Christian religion or the Buddist religion, *et cetera*. It is further described as a state of mind or way of life expressing love for and trust in God, and one's will and effort to act according to the will of God, especially within a specific church or community. It goes on to say that this is an effort of conscientious regard and pursuit. This word comes from the Latin stem religare, meaning to bind back, or to bind together, and is seen in the Greek as a word meaning "to pay heed to."

Now it should be obvious that without this *sincere* belief; without this expression of belief and conduct; without this philosophy, state of mind, and way of life, which expresses love and trust, we cannot really have a true "religion." That is the reason this book was written, for modern research shows us that it is basically through hypnotic techniques in any, all, and every religion that we are able to bind back that religion to ourselves, to pay heed to it and to derive benefit from it. Although all religions will be generally covered, I will be primarily concerned with the Christian religion to which I subscribe.

Now the last two sentences will no doubt cause a storm of protest among those who are not familiar with what hypnosis is and what it means. Let us now take the word hypnosis and attempt to adequately define it. Here we have a real misconception that has been brought down through the ages. In one of the latest non-technical dictionaries, hypnosis is defined as "a sleep-like condition psychically induced, usually by another person, in which a person loses consciousness, but responds with certain limitations to the suggestion of the hypnotist." *Nothing could be further from the truth.* In the first place, Webster is wrong in saying that it is a sleep-like condition. The word was coined by Braid in 1842 from the Greek word "hypnos," meaning sleep. Braid thought at first that this was the case. He later realized that, far from being asleep, the subjects had closed their eyes in order to super-concentrate their minds on one idea, and hence he tried to change the name, calling the phenomenon "mono-ideaism." But the term "hypnosis," misdescriptive as it was, had already stuck to the phenomenon and hence, soon became generally used.

Furthermore, since in a state of hypnosis, a person's eyes are closed, the popular misconception that the subject was asleep has continued. The subject is no more asleep in hypnosis (just because he has his eyes closed) than you are asleep in church when you are standing in prayer with your eyes closed and head bowed. You are actually in the same state, a state of hypnosis, a state of mono-ideaism, in which your one idea and thought is (or at least it should be) concentrated on God. It states, in the dictionary, that the subject loses consciousness. Let me state categorically, that from the beginning of time no subject under hypnosis ever loses consciousness unless, of course, he goes to sleep, in which case he is not under hypnosis. Despite the fact that we use the word "sleep" to induce patients into a "hypnotic sleep," there is no loss of consciousness in this hypnotic sleep, and while it has certain similarities with regular sleep (especially that state of regular sleep in which there are dreams), the mind is super-concentrating and is extremely active, even more so than in the waking state.

PART 2. DEFINITION OF HYPNOSIS

What, then, is a good definition of hypnosis? As I have stated elsewhere, hypnosis is a normal physiological phenomenon; an altered state of consciousness, similar to but not the same as being awake; similar to but not the same as being asleep. Hypnosis is produced by the presence of two conditions: (1) a central focus of attention, and (2) surrounding areas of inhibition. The state of hypnosis, in turn, produces three things: (1) an increased concentration of the mind; (2) an increased relaxation of the body; and (3) an increased susceptibility to suggestion.

Now let us examine the definition in detail. After rereading the definition of hypnosis just given in the previous sentence it is easy to see that by limiting the electronic activity of the brain to one specific concentrated point we achieve the state of hypnosis or, as Braid preferred to call it, "monoideaism." This is achieved in many ways, both purposefully and accidentally, both in response to suggestions from others and suggestions made by oneself. Examples in our everyday life are numerous. One example is "highway hypnosis," caused by concentration on the white line and surrounding areas on inhibition, while the rest of the body is seated and relaxed. This sort of hypnosis is obviously quite dangerous to us, and engineers have done a great deal of work to design highways which break up the monotony of driving, in order to prevent this state from occurring. On the other hand, medical hypnosis, as experienced in the physician's office (like prayer experienced in church) is highly beneficial. The important difference in a result may be due to the subject on which one's mind is concentrating. We can, therefore, define prayer now as merely a state of hypnosis in which the mind is super-concentrated on God. We will speak more of this later on.

It is important, however, for the layman to understand that hypnosis is a normal phenomenon available to all. It is neither black-magic nor witchcraft; but, on the contrary, a state of extreme concentration which, when focused upon God, enables us to become closer to Him and experience emotionally the great spiritual truths which we have been taught on a purely intellectual basis. This emotional rebirth in religion, accomplished through hypnosis, is necessary for a complete understanding of the universe on an organic level.

Hypnosis, however, is more than just an altered state of consciousness, just as religion is more than a state of mind. Hypnosis is a method by which we can investigate the deepest part of our minds, that part from which we normally cannot extricate memories in the waking state.

Isaiah 65:17, states: "For behold, I create new heavens,

and a new earth, and the former shall not be remembered, nor come into mind." We know that the former (namely heaven)[1] has been described many times by visions seen by many prophets. These visions were real, and the reason that it was possible to remember and bring back into the conscious mind the conditions which existed in the heaven from which we came, and from which we bring our soul to accompany us on a short journey through life on earth is that, through hypnosis or concentration of the mind, we do not use just the power of our waking conscious state. We use the great deep spiritual power that is within us; all the power, of the deepest part of our minds and souls in order to "remember."

What happens when we place the mind in a state of hypnosis? The mind, like the brain, is composed of units. The single unit of the brain is the cell, an anatomical unit, a unit of mass, which can be weighed. The single unit of the mind, however, cannot be weighed. It is a unit of power or energy and these individual units of mind power taken collectively, form the mind, an organ of energy, located within the brain. This mind energy or mind power, stored in some fantastic mechanism of chemistry and electronics which we have, as yet, not completely unravelled, is responsible for our memory, our behavior, and is the spiritual power which leaves the body on death and returns to the heaven from whence it came. We know the anatomical part of the body is dust and shall return to dust. It makes sense, then, that it is mental energy or mind power which forms the greater part of soul power.

Dr. Van Pelt has explained the phenomenon of suggestibility in hypnosis by means of a diagram which he has kindly given us permission to reprint (See Fig. 1). God, who is within us, influences us constantly through hypnotic suggestion (if we will only let him) in order to keep our lives untroubled and

1 Some theological scholars have interpreted this prophecy of Isaiah to mean that the former earth and heaven will not be remembered when God creates a new Heaven and Earth. Even with this interpretation however the concept which follows is not invalidated. All quotations from the Bible are taken from the Standard King James Version of 1611.

THE NATURE OF HYPNOSIS

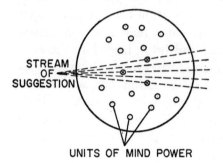

STREAM
OF
SUGGESTION

UNITS OF MIND POWER

ORDINARY STATE

Only a few "Units" affected
by Suggestion, therefore
effect is weak.

Scattered units of mind power untouched by suggestion.

HYPNOSIS

Units of mind power concentrated
and all affected by suggestion,
therefore strong effect.
No mind power left to take notice
of anything apart from the hypnotic suggestion, therefore even
pain is ignored.

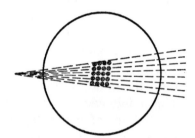

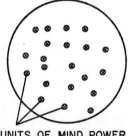

Units of mind power
scattered again but
now each carries a
dose of suggestion.

**AFTER
HYPNOSIS**

UNITS OF MIND POWER WITH
A DOSE OF SUGGESTION

FIGURE 1

This figure shows that hypnosis is neither sleep nor unconsciousness but
a superconcentration of the mind. It explains clearly why suggestion is
more powerful in hypnosis than in the ordinary state. (Reprinted cour-
tesy of Dr. S. J. Van Pelt, London, England.)

free from anxiety. Indeed, all we have to do is to merely keep our mind concentrated on Him. Isaiah tells us this in Chapter 26, Verse 3: "Thou wilt keep him in perfect peace whose mind is stayed on thee, because he trusteth in thee."

Every individual begins life as a single cell, and within this single cell there is a vast memory. This cell "remembers" and reproduces every physical characteristic of the parent cells, whose union produced it. It remembers that it is a human being and not a dog or cat; it remembers in its genes and chromosomes that it is going to turn into a little blonde-haired, blue-eyed boy with two hands, two feet, two eyes, a nose, and all the other millions of characteristics that a little boy must have. That, furthermore, this little boy is going to look like, act like, and be something like his parents. Is it not logical, then, to assume that, if one single cell has the capability of so much memory in so small a space, can we not, as adults, use those huge, silent areas of the brain for which no man has yet found the function? Can we not, as adults, concentrate the energy of millions of units of mind power, residing somewhere within the brain, in order to produce a union with God which brings about the perfect peace, tranquility, and understanding about which, and to which, the Bible constantly alludes?

When we realize that all visual perception actually takes place within the visual cortex located in the posterior portion of our brain, is it not reasonable to assume that, with proper concentration of our minds through the use of hypnosis, we can produce, artificially, the same electronic stimulation along the nerves of the optic tract to give us a vision that is fully as real as if we were receiving the stimulation from our eyes which had in turn been stimulated by photons of light reflected from the object being viewed? Indeed, in our imagination, with proper concentration of the mind, we can visualize, clearly and truly, scenes more beautiful, more real, and more complete than even exist on this earth. It should be obvious that we are merely, in this case, remembering the heaven from which we came. This part of the mind, however, is generally buried deep within us in a part of the brain unusable except through the use of hypnotic techniques. In the 103rd Psalm, David began by saying: "Bless the Lord, oh my soul." Now, in ancient Hebrew, to bless meant to kneel as an act of adoration. It meant humility, meekness, and love, but it also meant something else. "Bless" was very close to the word "bloody," and the ancient Hebrews thought life resided in blood, so the biblical meaning of blood meant "to give life to."

When translated in this fashion we realize that our soul does give life to the Lord. David says, "All that is within me bless his holy name" (Psalm 103:1) and it has been said, "Ye shall seek me and find me when ye shall search for me with *all* your heart" (Jer. 29:13). All these biblical quotations bear out the original premise that, without a central focus of attention, without this *concentration* of the mind through the use of hypnotic techniques, indeed, without hypnosis itself, there is no contact with God. There is no religion, there is nothing, and that all life is reduced only to our physical existence on earth, thereby losing its meaning.

It is through hypnosis that we concentrate this driving, living, breathing, dynamic, mental, soulful, powerful force within us, which keeps us in communion with the Creator at all times.

With a slightly clearer picture of both hypnosis and religion, let us now turn to some of the Church's viewpoints on the subject, in order to determine more effectively the relationship between the two.

Chapter II

VIEWS ON HYPNOSIS
BY VARIOUS FAITHS

PART 1. THE CATHOLIC FAITH

The late Pope Pius gave his approval to the use of hypnosis on several occasions. He stated that the use of hypnosis by physicians and dentists for diagnosis and treatment was permitted, but that it was not permitted for Catholics to enter into hypnosis for entertainment purposes. In an article entitled, "Hypnosis as Anaesthesia." by the Reverend Gerald Kelly, S.J., that appeared in *Hospital Progress*, December, 1957 issue, he lists the following quotations: The first quotation from the Vatican is from an address given to an audience of physicians on January 8, 1956, on the use of hypnosis in childbirth. Reverend Kelly summarized the Pope's three cardinal points as follows: "1. Hypnotism is a serious scientific matter, and not something to be dabbled in. 2. In its scientific use the precautions dictated by both science and morality are to be heeded. 3. Under the aspect of anaesthesia, it is governed by the same principle as any other form of anaesthesia." This amounts to saying that the rules of good medicine apply to the use of hypnotism; and in so far as its use conforms to these rules, it is in conformity with good morality.

In an earlier publication called *Moral and Pastoral Theology* by Father Henry Davis, S. J., published by Scheed and Ward, Father Davis states: "One may submit to hypnotic treatment for a grave reason if proper precautions are taken, and if there is no scandal." This, of course, was an older term meaning superstition. It is apparently no longer necessary to have a "grave" reason for submitting to hypnotic treatment, but only necessary that the "Rules of good medicine apply to the use

11

of hypnotism." Father Davis goes on to say that the hypnotist should be above reproach, and that a trustworthy witness should be present. This has been taken to mean that the hypnotist should be a qualified practicing physician or dentist, and that at least one other person should be present somewhere within the doctor's offices. This does not mean that persons undergoing analysis under hypnosis, hypnotic treatment or for any other reason should necessarily have a third party in the same room; since the presence of a third party obviously renders difficult any hypno-analytical treatment designed to delve into the patient's subconscious to any considerable depth.

As Dr. F. A. Evis has said, in the October, 1960 issue of the *Journal of the American Institute of Hypnosis,* "Incidentally, religious leaders endorse the use of hypnosis for medical treatment and dental purposes, and are unanimous in condemning its use for entertainment purposes and the practice of it by unqualified amateurs."

PART 2. THE JEWISH FAITH

There have been no objections to the use of hypnosis in the Jewish faith to date, provided that hypnosis is used as a medical tool for the benefit of mankind. It has been pointed out by various Rabbis that hypnosis could be misused and abused by unqualified hypnotists. Rabbi Glassner is perhaps one of the more famous Jewish religious leaders who has been familiar with hypnosis and hypnotic techniques and utilized them in his work. In fact, Rabbi Glassner, a doctor of education, has lectured at various seminars throughout the country on the subject of hypnosis and religion to various physicians and dentists.

PART 3. THE PROTESTANT FAITH

There have been no objections, by any of the main Protestant Church bodies, to the use of hypnosis in medicine and dentistry, and the question of healing has been left largely to the medical profession with, of course, the one principle exception reserved by all faiths, and that is the power of prayer.

Nevertheless, there are two churches which are commonly associated with the Protestant faith, which have been opposed to the use of hypnosis in the past. One church has since modified its ideas somewhat, but the other apparently remains unalterably opposed to it.

The first group are the Seventh Day Adventists, whose Washington spokesman, R. L. Odum, stated at one time that he believed no one should exercise his will to control the senses of others, since Jesus said "Come unto me all ye that labour" (Matt. 11:28). Since that time a great deal more has been learned about hypnotism, and those persons who have been responsible for church policy and medical policy regarding the church have gained in their knowledge of hypnosis. They have realized that the complete control of the will is never attained in the hypnotic trance, and that one is free to accept or reject suggestions as he wishes. Realizing that accepting suggestions necessary for pain relief is both a beneficial and worthy contribution to medical science, the Seventh Day Adventist's medical school in Los Angeles, commonly known as the College of Medical Evangelists, has instituted "relaxation therapy" in some of their outpatient clinics, and it has been used by a number of Seventh Day Adventist physicians in the administration of anaesthesia, although it is seldom called by the name "hypnosis." It would seem that as a greater knowledge of the subject is uncovered, it should gain greater and greater acceptance among those of the Seventh Day Adventist faith. I deeply question the basic premise of Mr. Odum on the grounds that Jesus never said, "Come *only* unto me"; and there are many references where Jesus himself employed others to utilize his techniques for the benefit of the sick. One such example is His use of the Centurion (Matt. 8:13).

The Christian Science church is the only church, to my knowledge, which still remains unalterably opposed to the use of hypnosis; although occasionally some articles denouncing hypnosis have appeared in the *Watch Tower,* which is a publication of the Jehovah's Witnesses. It should be said that Jehovah's Witnesses is a denomination in which the members are unalterably opposed to blood transfusions, on the basis of a direct quotation from the Bible which they believe prohibits its use. Nevertheless, there are a good many Jehovah's Witnesses who have experienced the benefits of hypnotism and who praise its use. Despite the fact that some are against it, there is nevertheless no national policy of the Jehovah's Witnesses barring hypnosis from medical treatment. One of the reasons for this is that the word hypnotism, as such, has never been mentioned in the Bible. It, of course, could not have been mentioned in the Bible since the term was first invented by Braid in 1842. The phenomenon could have been, and is described as we shall see in succeeding chapters.

Returning to the problem of the Christian Science church, one may perhaps understand their point of view if we examine, carefully, the origin of their religious beliefs. Mary Baker Eddy, who founded the Christian Science faith, obtained many of her ideas from Phineas Quimby, who was a stage hypnotist of that era. Phineas Quimby, himself, was a very interesting and unusual personage, who not only gave Mary Baker Eddy most of her ideas for founding the Christian Science religion, but also founded a number of other faiths of his own, including the Unity Movement.

Mary Baker Eddy was born July 16, 1821, on a farm in New England of 17th Century Massachusetts settler stock. She was a delicate, fragile child and subject to hysterical seizures. Her nervous ailment, the pathology of which is not clear, helped her to get her own way. As the youngest in the family she was indulged by her father who kept her out of school a good deal, believing her brain to be abnormal. Her brother taught her Hebrew, Greek, and Latin, and she soon became an avid reader.

At seventeen she was received into the membership of the Congregational Church. At the same time she was under treatment by her family physician for her hysteria which he treated with mesmeric suggestions. In 1843 she married and moved to Charleston, South Carolina, but after a few months her husband died, and she was dependent on the charity of the local Masons. In September of 1844 she gave birth to George, her only child. She taught school for a while, but remained in ill health, without means, and soon became a chronic invalid. Her illness was termed "spinal weakness with spasmodic seizures," which apparently were of psychosomatic or psychoneurotic origin. Her father rocked her in his arms and finally made a huge cradle, for which someone was always found to keep it continuously rocking. Her four year old son was sent away to live with relatives.

In 1853, she married Dr. David Patterson, an itinerant dentist and homeopathist. He travelled a lot and left his ailing wife alone. Her husband soon was captured by Confederate soldiers and again she became a helpless invalid.

After three months in a sanitarium, she consulted a Dr. Phineas Quimby, who had acquired some local fame for his cures through the use of hypnotism. In October of 1862, she went to his office, a rather pitiful figure. Three weeks later, in a letter published to the Portland Courier, she declared that by virtue of the great principle discovered by Dr. Quimby, "who speaks as never a man has spoken and heals as never a man has healed since Christ," she was on the way to complete health. She returned to her sister's home a confirmed disciple of Quimby.

In 1866 Quimby died, but, continuing his work, she taught and wrote regarding "the science of mind." Her first students paid $100 for their lessons (a tidy sum in those days). She later raised the fee to $300 for twelve lessons, dropped Quimby's name, and used her own exclusively in writing and expounding the metaphysical theories which were to become the doctrine of the Christian Science Church.

It is my personal belief, therefore, that in her zeal to gain acceptance for her new religion, Mary Baker Eddy found it

necessary to divorce herself entirely from the mysticism which
had grown to surround hypnotism as used on the stage during
that particular period. Without doing this she would have been
unable to gain the support of other members dedicated to her
faith. Therefore, even though she herself recognized that many
of the techniques used by the Christian Science Church itself
were actually the same as those used then by many stage
hypnotists, and that by various methods of concentration one
was expected to bring about changes in mental and physical
health (which is the exact method of using hypnosis in medicine today), she nevertheless had to denounce the very thing
which she was advocating in order to gain acceptance for her
particular faith. It must, she felt, be presented as a religion and
not as a technique, and she also rightly supposed that what was
permitted on the stage would not be permitted in the church so
therefore, a new label had to be attached to an old technique.
It is unfortunate that this continuity of lack of knowledge regarding the meaning of hypnosis and its proper usage persists
in the present day and age of the advancement of medical
science.

One would suppose that a church employing the name of
Chirstian Science would be the first group to advance their
ideas along with the advancement of science. It appears, however, that the group involved is extremely conservative and
has changed their basic dogma little from the time when it
was first laid down by Mary Baker Eddy. It is hoped that as
the responsible officials of this church gain a better knowledge
of the use of hypnosis in medicine, that they, too, will follow
the action of all other major Christian churches in approving
its use in medicine and dentistry.

PART 4. OTHER FAITHS

Many of the faiths of the Far East have not only approved
the use of hypnotic techniques, but actually depend upon them
to a great degree; both in the training of their priests and in
the maintenance of control over their congregations. The

parallels between the techniques of hypnosis and the philosophy of Yoga are obvious and have been discussed elsewhere. Hypnotic techniques in the utilization of a state of concentration in order to eliminate the stresses of the material world, are more or less common to all religions, but are especially evident in the Buddhist faith. The coöperation of Buddhist and Shinto priests in tending one another's temples in Japan offers a common meeting ground for the exchange of techniques of hypnotic concentration during prayer. There is a daily Moslem ritual of auto-suggestion, bowing towards Mecca, which reinforces their faith in Mohammed and his teachings by means of a continuing auto-suggestion.

Chapter III

THE VARIOUS APPEARANCES OF HYPNOSIS IN RELIGION

Rabbi Glassner has stated in the past that there are four connections between hypnosis and religion, which are: (1) the natural connection between the two phenomena; (2) the research into phenomena and nature of religion through the use of hypnosis; (3) the religious healing and hypnosis; (4) the use of hypnosis by the clergy in pastoral counselling.

James Esdaile recognized the connection between hypnosis and religion in at least three different ways.

First of all, he insisted that hypnosis was a natural God-given method of healing, as exemplified by the following quotation from his book, *Mesmerism in India:*

"As far as Mesmerism being a new and unnatural art, there is every reason to believe that it is the oldest and most natural mode of curing many of the severe, uncomplicated diseases of the human race. Let us imagine for a moment the condition of savage men, before, by long experience, they had learned to avail themselves of the medicinal virtues of the vegetable and mineral kingdoms, for the cure of their most pressing diseases. Man, in this state, should be more helpless than the brute creation; they have happy instincts, many of them known to us, by which they are directed not only to their natural food, but to their natural medicines. But man, so far as we yet know him, could in his sufferings only make vague experiments on the natural objects around him, in the desperate hope of stumbling upon some suitable remedy. This might occasionally happen, but he was more likely to be poisoned than cured by his first experiments. The very fish were more favored than he. The salmon, by an infallible instinct, quit the sea at a certain season, and ascend the rivers, thereby getting rid of their tormentors, the sea-lice (which the fresh water speedily kills,) and at the same time reaching the spots destined for the propagation of their kind.

After depositing the spawn, the parent fish, black, lank, and sick, distasteful to themselves, and unwholesome to us, hasten to the sea to renovate their health; whence, again, they issue in another year, increased in size, and brilliant as silver, to run the same course as long as life continues. The young fry, also, the moment they break the egg, turn their heads seaward, and never stop till they reach the ocean, whose action is necessary for their growth and health.

The dog eats grass, and licks his sores when sick; the cow, and calf even, sham dead, to induce the crows to pick the vermin from about their eyes and ears; the chick, as soon as it breaks the shell, pecks gravel to aid digestion; the mongoose, after being bitten by its enemy the snake, retires to the fields, to seek its antidote against the poison, and this it finds, for it comes back quite well; and at certain seasons the wild animals resort, from the most distant parts of the country, to the 'salt-licks,' to renovate their constitutions. Numberless instances of the same kind will occur to the naturalist, and the humble observer of nature even; and is it imaginable that the ever-watchful all-bountiful Providence of God should have run such cruel risks, and perish helplessly in his natural ignorance? Reasoning, a priori, we should say not; and our positive knowledge of the equal care bestowed by God on all His creatures, forbids the supposition. Man, then, had probably some instinct by which he was directed to a natural medicine of sovereign virtue, and by which the hunter and his family were saved from starvation, when disease, for a time, deprived his right hand of its cunning, unnerved his iron sinews, and bowed his gallant head. If this be a natural supposition, what could be his resource if not Mesmerism — that inherent power, implanted, as I conceive, in the human being, for the solace of his suffering fellow creature? This is the simplest and most speedy restorative of the powers of life, in cases adapted to it (for, like every natural agent, it has its conditions and limits); and men in pain have an instinctive tendency to perform the required processes. From its simplicity, how consonant with all we know of the laws of nature would be such a power, and how admirably adapted to meet the exigencies of savage life."

The second reference to hypnosis in religion occurs when Esdaile likens the power of the Creator to the power produced by the unconscious mind of a person under hypnosis. Futhermore, Esdaile points out quite clearly that the objections to the use of hypnosis in medicine, because it might be injudiciously administered, are ignorant and unreasonable, since these same objections might well be applied to the use of any medicine or procedure:

"The possible evil resulting to society from the practice of Mesmerism has been a favorite objection even when the evidence of its existence and power could no longer be resisted. But the tendency of all power depends upon the direction given to it for good, or evil; and to eject opium, mercury, and prussic acid from the pharmacopoeia, because, when injudiciously administered, they poison instead of curing our patients; or to reject the agency of steam for the purposes of life, because it sometimes takes us a longer journey than we intended; would be as reasonable as to refuse to be cured by Mesmerism, because it could also injure us, if ignorantly and injudiciously applied. That this agent may, and will, be turned to the most diabolical purposes, is most certain, if the public will not be at the trouble to think upon the subject, and defend itself by common sense precautions. But the power as it comes from the Creator is pure, and the perversion of it is the work of the creature. The object of man's life here clearly is — to separate the good from the evil; 'to prove all things, and hold fast to that which is good'; and this can be done in Mesmerism, as in anything else; the abuse, and not the use of any great power, is to be dreaded and guarded against."

The third reference to hypnosis in religion by Esdaile occurs on page thirty-nine of his book, in which he alludes to the universal benevolence of the Deity in the creation of his creatures, and the fact that Mesmerism is a natural power of man. Here he states:

"The Father of Medicine thought very differently from his degenerate sons, for he says, 'Nothing should be omitted in an art which interests the whole world, which may be beneficial to suffering humanity, and which does not risk human life and comfort.' But a time was, when apothecaries, chemists, and diploma'd physicians did not exist; when man was an unreasoning animal, devoid of all the resources of art, yet subject to all the ills that natural flesh is heir to; and it is a subject of deep interest to the philosopher and the physician to ascertain what were his natural remedies, in common with the other animals; whether his instincts were as strong as theirs, and to what conservative powers he resorted when laboring under disease. That he possessed such appears to me to be extremely probable, from the analogies of the animal creation, and the universal benevolence of the Deity to his creatures. It must be most important and instructive to discover what were, or if not yet known, what are, the natural remedies of man; for by observing their effects we shall best understand the restorative processes of Nature, and be able to imitate them by art, with a certainty hitherto unattained by medicine."

James Esdaile therefore recognized three cardinal points where hypnotism (which he called Mesmerism) and Religion were in agreement. In summary the points are as follows:

1. Hypnosis was a natural God-given method of healing.
2. The power produced by the unconscious mind of one under Hypnosis is similar both in quality, character, and degree with the power of the Creator.
3. The Universal Benevolence of the Deity is such that all of his creatures carry, instilled within them, great powers to direct their movement and provide for themselves. The power of hypnotism is one of the great powers instilled in man for this purpose.

Hypnosis, like Religion, is therefore *Natural, Powerful* and *Universal.*

As we have said before, the term hypnosis was not used until Braid coined it in 1842, but the principles of hypnosis have, of course, been used for years. *Suggestion in der Welt Psychologie,* by Dr. Stoll, marks the first mention of hypnosis as such in religion. Theodore Wright described hypnosis as it occurred in savage cultures, such as the puberty rites of the African tribes in the Congo, in which boys were put into a trance and, after some weeks, reawaken with complete amnesia for their past life, and have a new name. It is interesting that this idea of rebirth is a part of every major religion throughout the world. There seems to be a general feeling among all peoples of the world, who have grown up independently of one another in many different geographical and ecclesiastical areas, that it is apparently necessary to be "born again" if one expects to reach the Kingdom of God, or any other postulate state of immortality.

Furthermore, this rebirth must consist of an emotional rather than an intellectual experience, and one may talk about it, discuss it, argue it, and indeed, research it on every technological sense from an intellectual viewpoint and still not experience it. It is the emotional experience that is necessary in order to cleanse the soul; and this, of course, is a direct parallel to hypnosis and hypno-analytical methods, since it explains so easily why patients, when they come to the physician's office, may very well state to the physician, "Doctor, I know what my trouble is, but I still can't do anything about it." The answer is of course, that they may have an intellectual idea of the trouble, but they have never experienced the analysis of the problem on an *emotional* level. As we have said before, it is emotion which concentrates the mind. It is only at the emotional level of the subconscious mind where one may introduce strong hypnotic suggestive ideas, and may also remove other strong negative hypnotic suggestions which may have previously been planted there by accident.

Returning, now, to the idea of rebirth, when one sincerely begins over again on an emotional level, one gains a great deal of inner peace and contentment from the fact that the sins of the past no longer apply and that out of gratitude for such relief one may therefore actually achieve the state of communion with the Diety desired.

The prophets produced their visions by a form of auto-hypnosis, and in the Middle Ages most of the prophets who heard the voice of God actually dissociated their own voices and heard themselves. The visions of Ezekiel and Daniel were definitely produced by auto-hypnosis, and men were shown in dreams what was suggested to them by their own thoughts.

In the eighteenth century a Catholic priest, named Father Gassner, used to cast out devils with hypnosis, and he was a direct predecessor and teacher of Mesmer. This came about as follows:

Mental illness was frequently referred to in the Bible and throughout the Middle Ages in the terms that such a patient was possessed by devils, or that his mind was possessed by devils. To cure a patient of mental illness the devils had to be cast out, and it would seem, or at least it did seem at that time, that the proper person to call upon to do this would be a religious leader. Father Gassner gained a great reputation for his ability to cure mental illness in this fashion, and his method was to enter a church in long flowing black robes, carrying a large brass cross. The suffering parishoner had long since been brought into the church, made to kneel down, close his eyes and await the good priest. While in this state of meditation he would be given the suggestion by one of Father Gassner's assistants, to wit, that whenever Father Gassner touched him with the brass cross, the devils would immediately be cast out. Besides this final suggestion, he had been previously receiving many indirect suggestions regarding the good Father's potent powers during every step of the preparations, which were both lengthy and ritualistic in character. Before the entrance of the Father a number of spectators were ushered into an area to witness the cure first hand. This, of course, gave a certain publicity to the power of the Church, to the wonders worked by Father Gassner, and also created additional motivation in the patient by virtue of the fact that all these people had come to see the cure, and therefore he "must deliver." Furthermore, these witnesses were not just laymen but were frequently high officials of the Church, as well as visiting medical clinicians. It was on one of these days, when Father Gassner was casting out devils, that Mesmer chanced to attend such a session. He described it as being almost like a theatrical performance. The patient was ushered in, carefully prepared by the assistants after a previously well-rehearsed ritual, and then, as if on cue, Father Gassner majestically entered the room and lowered the cross onto the head of the patient. The patient immediately collapsed, then rose to his feet, praised God and announced that he was well.

This type of direct suggestion impressed Mesmer a great deal and, in fact, was the very thing that led him to suspect that the power to cure mental illness rested not necessarily with the religious nature of the cross but with some other property which it possessed. Since the cross was made out of metal, Mesmer theorized that if the arms of the cross were left off, perhaps it would still perform the same feat. It was this idea that led him to his experiments in animal magnetism which, of course, eventually resulted in the publication of his famous paper which in turn was responsible for driving him out of Vienna.

It is of course interesting to note the evolution of a theory, and just as Father Gassner had been wrong in supposing that it was the cross which was responsible for casting out the devils, so had Mesmer been wrong in supposing that it was the metal contained in the cross which was responsible for eliminating the mental illness of the patient. It remained, therefore, for Braid to revise Mesmer's theory, postulating that it was actually the suggestive influence and its acceptance by the patient that was responsible. This theory has held solid until the present day. It is, of course, entirely possible that in the future it too may be supplanted by an even better theory regarding the processes by which hypnotic treatment is successful, but that it *is* successful, and exceedingly successful, no one has ever seriously questioned.

Many theologians of that era used auto-hypnosis to deepen their own religious experience enabling them to remain closer to their own personal Gods. Many elements of hypnosis remain in our religion today. The chanting, testimonials, the flickering candles and the cross as a fixation point for our vision; the relaxation of the rest of our body; the bowing of our heads in supplication; the silence in the Friend's meeting; Kavanah[2] in Jewish mysticism; the preparation for prayer; the rotation of the body in the synagogue, and the effect of prayer on those who offer it, are all examples of hypnotic techniques which have been accepted as part of our own religious experience. Both prayer and religious healing will be discussed later, but in this general discussion of hypnosis in religion a few isolated facts still remain which are of interest historically. The first tooth extraction, using hypnosis, was accomplished by Dr. Wortman of Boston. Dr. Ellwood Worchester and Dr. Elmer Mitchell, a minister and an M. D., respectively, started a church based on hypnotic principles which gradually petered out in the 1920's and 1930's.

The use of hypnosis in pastoral counselling has made tremendous strides in late years, especially since its approval by the American Medical Association. Some ministers have been shying away from the term due to the implication of the dangers involved, but actually most ministers either employ hypnosis or hypnotic techniques in prayer and practically this same thing in all their counselling with the members of their various congregations. It is unthinkable that, after discussing a particularly serious problem with a minister, the minister does not require the person who came to him for help

2 *Auto-Hypnotic Aspects of the Jewish Cabbalistic Concept of Kavanah,* by Margaretta K. Bowers M.D. and Rabbi Samuel Glassner.

to pray for a solution. Invariably a better result occurs if the minister and the person involved begin by praying together right at that very moment, so that hypnotic techniques are immediately brought into play and the father/son relationship to the Diety is immediately utilized for utmost benefits. It is my considered opinion that the use of hypnotic techniques throughout the various ministries of this country for the benefit of mankind would be a tremendously beneficial project, which should be undertaken at the earliest possible moment. It would certainly be of aid in increasing the effectiveness of prayer.

Chapter IV

HYPNOSIS AND PRAYER

"The effect of prayer upon those who offer it could well
be made a matter of scientific research."
. . . . KARL MENNINGER[3]

The fact that prayer as well as some idea of rebirth forms a part of every major religion the world over, and supplies a universal need of the individual, should certainly bring to mind the necessity for examining the mechanism of prayer under an ecclesiastical and intellectual "microscope" to determine from whence this great value comes, and how it can best be utilized for the benefit of mankind everywhere. Certainly no one living in the 20th century would question the value of frequent prayer. One needs only to examine the lives of those persons who pray daily to discover that they are also the people who are the most secure, the most stable, and who have the best control over the stresses, strains, and problems which invariably occur in any lifetime.

Persons soundly rooted in their Church, praying daily and trusting in God, are somehow able to endure a great deal more stress than those who do not have this firm mental rudder. Since both the value and the need of prayer are universally recognized, it would seem important to turn to the dissection of this interesting phenomenon and, by getting some idea of its parts, try to understand the whole. It is, of course, axiomatic that one can never understand the whole of anything by *only* examining the parts. Hence, for example, if one enters the shop of a watchmaker and examines only the wheels, latches, hands and crystal of a watch all torn apart, one still does not

3 Menninger, Karl A.: Religio Psychiatri in *Religion and Human Behavior,* edited by Simon Doniger, New York. Association Press, 1954, Page 3.

27

get the idea that a watch is an instrument used to tell time. However, one can get the idea that the watch is an instrument made up of certain parts which, when put together, are expected to move in a certain way. Therefore, while it is true we cannot understand the whole by only examining the parts, neither can we understand the parts by only examining the whole. And so, of necessity, both investigations must be undertaken.

Regarding the composition of prayer, one must first take into consideration the preparation for the experience. In almost every church this preparation includes the assuming of a certain definite prescribed position. Although the positions vary greatly from religion to religion, the position nevertheless in some manner or another indicates the supplication of the parishioner. That is to say, in analyzing the position for prayer, whether it be lying on the ground, kneeling, or even standing, the head is generally bowed. The palms of the hands may be placed together, at one's side, or firmly on the ground, but in any case the general "feeling" of the particular position assumed is one of supplication either to some *thing* or some *one* (generally the Deity).

Now why is this so? It apparently is necessary that when one asks a favor of a power greater than oneself, one is expected to behave in a fashion which recognizes the fact that said power has the right either to grant or refuse; and, therefore, it is plain good sense to ask, and at the same time thank him for past favors, rather than to demand. It is significant that in no state of prayer in any religion in the world is the fist ever clenched. There are other factors which are similar to this state of prayer which belong to the preparation thereof, and relate to the physical position of the participant. One of these is the fact that in all states of prayer the muscles of the body are always relaxed, so that no matter what position is assumed, it nevertheless must be a position in which the person can relax *all* the muscles of his body. This also creates another reason why no religion in the world prays with clenched fists, while standing on one foot, *et cetera*.

This relaxation of the body immediately triggers a thought within us that this is *one* of the conditions necessary to enter the hypnotic trance. Therefore, one would expect to encounter in prayer a number of the phenomena similarly encountered in hypnosis. We find, on further examination, that an even greater similarity exists because the other condition necessary for entrance into the hypnotic trance, namely, the central focus of attention on a particular thing, object or idea, is also met during prayer, *i.e.*, the simple focus of attention in this case is invariably on the Deity.

Therefore, by thoroughly examining the elements of prayer, we find that these same elements are present on entering a hypnotic trance, and that what is actually happening is that, in order for prayer to be effective, it is actually necessary to enter a hypnotic trance. The hypnotic trance of prayer is no different from the hypnotic trance encountered in the physician's office, except that the hypnotic trance encountered in the physician's office may be produced in a variety of ways, while the hypnotic trance of prayer is invariably produced in the same way, namely by the central focus of attention on God, with surrounding areas of inhibition of the body musculature. One cannot expect results from prayer if one does not enter into an emotional communication with the Diety, and this cannot be achieved while one is scratching one's ear, combing one's hair, or moving any other parts of the voluntary muscular system. It is exactly the same as in hypnosis, *i.e.*, one needs not only the central focus of attention but also the surrounding areas of inhibition. People who do not have both prerequisites only think they are praying, and have never really experienced the benefit of prayer at all.

It is further noteworthy that most praying is done with the eyes closed, and that as the prayer ends it is usually brought to a close by the saying of a familiar phrase (*e.g.*, the Amen used in Christian churches), which serves as a wake-up signal and allows the parishioner to then open his eyes. It is exactly the same in hypnosis. One can always open their eyes if they really want to, but the answer to the question is invariably "I just didn't feel as if I wanted to open my eyes." This is the same reason why persons in prayer invariably keep their eyes shut until the end of the prayer, and that those who don't keep their eyes closed break the trance, thereby breaking their close contact with God at the same time, and losing the benefit lying therein.

It is important, then, that we should investigate and dissect the subject of prayer. In any religion prayer consists primarily of a communion with a deity, and this is accomplished invariably through the use of hypnotic techniques. It is interesting that we have a parallel between the brain and the mind and the body and the soul, in that the brain is the anatomical unit which controls the body, and the mind is the psychophilosophical unit somewhere within the brain. The body, on the other hand, is generally understood to be the anatomical house in which the psychophilosophical unit of the soul exists. It should be quite conceivable then to suppose that upon the death of the brain and the body that both the mind and the soul (being psychophilosophical units rather than anatomical ones) might very well leave their anatomical houses at approximately the same time, and therefore the individuality of each soul is preserved in heaven through its accompanying partner, the mind. If this is true, a study of the mind should bring to light a great deal of evidence about the soul, and vice-versa. Thus by reaching into the deeper portions of the mind (as in the analysis of the subconscious through hypnosis), we should also be able to occasionally glance into the deeper reaches of the soul (a fact which can be verified by any hypno-analyst with sufficient experience). Apparently, what is true of the mind is also frequently true of the soul, and as we might expect in moments of extreme emotional concentration, when the mind is greatly concentrated, we also find the soul is greatly concentrated. For this reason, in order to influence the soul, we must first concentrate the mind. It is under such moments of extreme mental concentration that an emotional experience takes place. This emotional experience, when given proper direction and motivation, frequently results in a beneficial transformation of character.

It is because of this very well known fact we can suppose that on the occasion of great emotion one can concentrate the soul in the same manner that one can concentrate the mind, and that God may fill one's soul with powerful positive suggestions in the same manner that we may fill our minds with these same positive suggestions. If we assume that the soul is divided into units of soul power similar to those units of mind power (which make up the mind), this relationship is even easier to understand.

Let us now examine the way in which various things are accomplished through prayer. In order to accomplish anything with hypnosis, one must first be able to enter the hypnotic trance. In order to accomplish anything through prayer one must first be able to pray. In order to pray and pray effectively one must *learn* how in the same way that one *learns* how to enter the hypnotic trance. One best learns to pray from someone who already knows how to pray, in the same manner that one best learns hypnosis from someone who already understands it. As with hypnosis, prayer takes practice; and, as has been previously stated, it consists of concentrating the mind on one central focus of attention, namely a deity, and relaxing the rest of the voluntary musculature so as to create a surrounding area of electronic inhibition in the brain. Prayer, however, consists of more than just hypnosis alone; since, if it is truly prayer, it contains also a seriousness of purpose which may or may not be present during a hypnotic trance.

It is for this reason that neither prayer nor hypnosis should be approached from a light-hearted or frivolous point of view. It must be evident to the reader by now that both under hypnosis and under prayer great mental and physical changes can take place. It is this very fact which has led so often to the reiteration of the axiom that *"prayer changes things."* Prayer certainly does change things.

Many serious students of religion have frequently posed the question "Are all prayers really answered?" In the light of religious research through hypnotic techniques one can certainly answer in the affirmative, and do it with a method of proof. In the days of Mesmer many patients were treated by the Mesmeric method of simply concentrating the mind and relaxing the body to gain inner peace. During this period of Mesmeric treatment a great many of the patients received no suggestions whatsoever, and yet were benefited greatly. It seemed that each patient received what he particularly needed while he was "entranced" by the professional magnetizer. In the same way, therefore, we can postulate that even when prayers are completely wordless, the entering into an emotional communication with the Deity has a beneficial effect upon the individual. That, even if one does not ask for or receive everything (or even anything) that he has asked for, nevertheless, at a very minimum, he has received the benefits (both physically and mentally), which come from participating in a state which improves the physical and mental well-being of the individual. Prayer is a state of mind, an altered state of consciousness, a specific kind of hypnosis. The conversation of prayer is merely the communication between the mortal and his God.

In the preceding paragraphs we have illustrated how one can explain the fact that all prayers are actually answered, but there is a great deal more involved in the meaning of prayers than this. The fact that millions of individuals actually receive what they pray for supports the idea that if what one prays for is genuinely good for him, and if the prayer in itself is in earnest and properly executed, it will, quite amazingly, be frequently answered in the affirmative. "Therefore I say unto you, what things soever ye desire when ye pray, believe ye that ye receive them, and ye shall have them" . . . Mark 11:24. In order to receive the affirmative answer to one's prayer, it is important *to believe*. This can only be accomplished when it is done on a level of deep emotion within the recesses of the deepest parts of our mind and soul. This "sincere true belief" is only felt by the employment of hypnosis. Naturally, it must also be assumed that prayers can be answered negatively, that is to say, God has the power to say *No*. (He answered your prayer and the answer was, "No.")

The affirmative answer to a request during the state of prayer has to be explained on some rational basis which transcends the mystic. There are a number of explanations on a logical basis to account for the fact that prayer changes things. For instance, the man who prays for a raise in salary may soon find that through prayer he has improved himself enough to deserve one. His employer, seeing the man's increased value to his firm, offers him a raise in order to keep him. In the same manner, one may change one's personality or gain courage, peace of mind, and other attributes which he was formerly lacking. Also, since prayer teaches one concentration, the prayerful man is more likely to see and grasp opportunities which other men have allowed to lay dormant.

Everyone remembers the story of the soldier who, disgusted with his poor quality of sword, broke it in half and sulked away from the battlefield. On the other hand, the King, having lost his sword, seized the broken half and fought valiantly to defeat his enemies with the implement which was made available to him at that crucial moment.

The real ability of one to succeed where others fail lies in the control of the mind and the ability to utilize the power within. This is the fact which all great men have in common. One of the easiest methods to gain control of this mind power is by means of frequent prayer, coupled with the utilization of the results therefrom. Since, as we have said before, the mind is housed within the brain, and the soul within the entire body, it should be axiomatic that prayer must be done using the entire body as well as the brain; or, if you prefer, prayer must come from the soul as well as from the mind.

This means that our actions in prayer, as in the waking state, are as important as our words, if not more so. Our deeds, therefore, take on a new psychophysical meaning, when one couples them with the various thought processes. The organization of thoughts (and by this we mean the removal of thoughts to various organ systems) has been well documented by thousands of idioms in every language of the world. "He is a pain in the neck," and "I just can't stomach that," are just a few of the many examples which constantly remind us that brain and body are inseparable, in the same manner that mind and soul are one.

If we then accept this philosophy that mind and soul are really inseparable and exist together, then we must realize the tremendous influence of the one on the other, and the necessity of maintaining both in excellent health through prayer. If we finally reach this point, it is then important that we carry through in developing a program which will guarantee that we are able to utilize this great force for our own benefit, as well as for the benefit of mankind.

Since prayer, like hypnosis, is a technique which must be learned, it follows that it must also be taught. The question then, obviously, presents itself: "When is the best time to teach prayer?" The best time to choose one's doctor is before one becomes ill, and the best time to learn prayer is before one really feels the need of it. This time is in childhood. Indeed, the first thing a child should be taught is how to pray, since one learns more easily, more quickly, and retains more of what one learns during childhood than at any other time. Furthermore, during childhood the child is already in a state of chronic hypnosis. As William Wordsworth wrote in his ode *Intimations of Immortality*, "Heaven lies about us in our infancy," and children are much better able to visualize the Deity at this time than later on, when "man perceives the vision die away, and fades into the light of common day."

In the Moslem religion young Moslem boys are issued a prayer board, which they hang up in the mosque, and on which they kneel daily, reading the prayer printed in front of them on the other end of the board. They read monotonously and rhythmically, utilizing all the techniques of auto-hypnosis in order to deepen their religious experience through prayer. It is a pity that the Christian religion does not also have some concrete method of encouraging prayer among younger people, such as exists in the foregoing example. Dr. Raymond Lindquist, Pastor of the Hollywood Presbyterian Church has said, "Prayer is sometimes an *Escape,* an escape from a troubled world." Certainly this can also fit hypnosis. Hypnosis used for relaxation under proper medical direction can be highly beneficial. "Prayer can also be an *Enlistment.* We pray for orders from above." This corresponds to the cures resulting from hypnotherapy when patients *enlist* the aid of the therapist and *accept* his orders in the form of therapeutic suggestions. Most of all, Dr. Lindquist reminds us that "Prayer is *Enlargement,*" an enlargement in understanding and spiritual growth. This is also true of hypnotherapy which invariably brings with it a greater understanding of one's own mental and moral processes, as well as an intellectual and emotional growth both in bodily health and in spiritual strength.

In summary, then, what is prayer? Prayer actually consists of two things: the state of prayer and the communication of prayer. The state of prayer is an altered state of consciousness of the mind known also as hypnosis, except that it is limited to that state of hypnosis in which the concentration of the mind is focused upon the Deity. The communication which goes on between the mortal involved, and God, is also called by the noun, prayer, and may begin once the *state of prayer* is attained. This communication between God and the individual most frequently consists of (a) thanksgiving (b) confession and (c) appeal for future guidance on the part of the individual, as well as (a) answers, (affirmative and negative) (b) forgiveness and (c) orders on the part of the Deity.

Like the communications in hypno-analysis, answers and orders may either come from the God within you or from the

Father within the physician. There is, therefore, no essential
argument or quarrel between Catholic and Protestant systems
of prayer. Prayer, like hypnosis, works either directly or in-
directly through others, but it is essential both in prayer as in
other forms of hypnosis that a "rapport" exist. A communication must by definition be composed of two parties. The other
party is always there and available, but you must contact him
or no communication takes place. If the mortal is unable to
perceive the reply of the deity, it simply means he has not
properly prepared himself regarding his "state of prayer" and,
that in fact, no communication has really ever existed.

The emotional feeling of prayer on the soul, like the emotional feeling of hypnosis on the mind, has been expressed by
many writers. A few examples follow: James Montgomery,
the poet, said "Prayer is the soul's sincere desire . . . prayer is
the Christian's vital breath . . . Lord, teach us how to pray."
Charlotte Perkins Gilman, in her famous poem entitled *"Two
Prayers,"* asked for "Light to discover the way, power to follow
it long." John Niehardt, in his *Prayer For Pain,* implored,
"Grant this my only prayer — oh, keep my soul from turning
gray!" Prayer for the sanctity of one's own soul, (and hence
the mind as well), has been best expressed by Tennyson in his
prayer from *Idylls of The King* — "Pray for my soul . . . More
things are wrought by prayer than this world dreams of. Therefore let thy voice rise like a fountain for me night and day.
For what are men better than sheep or goats that nourish a
blind light within the brain, if, knowing God, they lift not
hands of prayer both for themselves and those who call them
friends? For so the whole round earth is every way bound by
golden chains about the feet of God."

Now this is not the sine qua non for prayer, and the fact
that a great many things still remain unexplained about it and
will no doubt remain unexplained for many years to come, is
a fact to be acknowledged. It is, however, through hypnotic
research that a great step forward has been achieved in ex-
plaining many things about prayer which have hitherto been

unexplained. Likewise, by researching the history of religious healing we uncover truths regarding hypnotism and man's earlier use of its powers. "Is any among you afflicted? Let him pray." (James 5:13.) "And the prayer of faith shall save the sick." (James 5:15.)

Chapter V

THE EVIDENCE OF JESUS USING HYPNOSIS TO HEAL

This particular chapter is inserted primarily for those followers of the Christian faith who feel that they need something from the Gospel for reassurance regarding the use of hypnosis in medicine. Hypnosis is probably the most natural method of healing in use today. It is older and more natural than drugs, operations, and x-ray. Yet because of its mystic character it has had a difficult time gaining acceptance by recognized medical authorities. This fortunately, now, is no longer the case, especially since the approval of hypnosis by the British Medical Association in 1955, and the subsequent approval by the American Medical Association in 1958.

Wolberg alludes to the importance of religion in the hypnotic treatment of alcoholics when he states: "Many alcoholics stop drinking when they feel that their dependency is appeased by an alliance with God. The religious cure of alcoholism is dynamically based on the drinker's conviction that if he lives up to God's expectations and stays sober, he will be given bounties and beneficences, if not now, then in the hereafter."[4]

It is my belief that the more important psycho-dynamic explanation of the cure is based upon the fact that the basic psycho-pathology of the alcoholic is composed of two problems: (a) the alcoholic is generally a patient with a deficient father figure and (b) it is well known that the alcoholic has a deficient ego. Religion supplies both of these psychological needs in the following way: (a) it offers the patient not only just a father figure but a real father figure greater than any

4 *Medical Hypnosis*, Vol. I, by Wolberg, page 336.

living human being, namely, "OUR FATHER which art in Heaven," and (b) by stressing the equality of all creatures under God, the ego of the patient becomes raised to the level of his associates. The importance of including the proper religious guidance in the treatment of any alcoholic cannot, therefore, be over-emphasized.[5]

Indeed, this fact has been recognized by Alcoholics Anonymous, and is included in their organization's program as a vital part of the rehabilitation of the alcoholic patient.

Hypnosis has made great strides in the healing arts. However, there are definite reasons for this; and we can go back two thousand years and find these reasons. The Holy Bible is simply studded with cases in which the Good Lord, Jesus Christ, Himself, chose methods of suggestion in order to heal the illnesses of his many followers. It was not called hypnosis, nor was it called Mesmerism. It was, in fact, called "casting out devils"; and sometimes it was not even called that. Nevertheless, Jesus Christ used hypnosis not once but many times, and some of the references regarding his use of the hypnotic techniques will follow, with an appropriate discussion of the medical problem involved, and how it was handled by the Man after whom the Christian religion was named—this Man who is believed by Christians to be the Son of God.

In Chapter 8 of the Gospel of St. Matthew, Verses 1 through 3, the Bible states: "When He was come down from the mountain, great multitudes followed Him. And behold, there came a leper and worshipped Him, saying, Lord, if Thou wilt, Thou canst make me clean. And Jesus put forth His hand and touched him saying, I will; be thou clean, and immediately his leprosy was cleansed."

Now, let us examine these verses. First of all, Jesus was among a great crowd of people, a group of followers who had an unquestioning faith in Jesus and in His ability. At this time a leper approached Him, worshipped Him, addressing Him as

5 *The Treatment of Alcoholism* by William J. Bryan Jr., M.D. Journal of the American Institute of Hypnosis, Vol. II, No. 1, January, 1961.

Lord, stating he had faith that Jesus could make him clean. Jesus gave him the direct suggestion when He said, "Be thou clean," and at the same time put forth His hand and touched him, which was the signal for the leper to become well.

Immediately the man was cured of leprosy. We hear no more about this man, and there were no doubt many cases of various dermatoses which were misdiagnosed as leprosy in those days, and were not true Hansen's disease. Whether this case was a case of Hansen's disease or not is difficult to prove, but in any case we can certainly be sure that at least the case was one in which there was visible evidence that dermatological lesions existed, because a great many people viewed them and left us records of what they observed at that particular time. These were healed by direct suggestion, and in a very short time, which, together with the examples below, constitute ample evidence of the use of hypnotic techniques by Christ.

We do know, however, that generally speaking, dermatological lesions respond well to hypnotic suggestion, and the quick disappearance of warts, allergies, rashes, hives, blisters, and other lesions by hypnotic suggestion is a proven fact. One of the reasons postulated regarding the rapid response of skin lesions to suggestions accepted through faith is because both the skin and the nervous system (through which the suggestions presumably operate) are derived from the same type of body cells, *i.e.*, they are both of ectodermal origin.

In the same Chapter, Verses 5 through 11, state: "And when Jesus was entered into Capernaum, there came unto Him a Centurian, beseeching Him, and saying, Lord, my servant lieth at home sick of the palsy, grieviously tormented. And Jesus sayeth unto him, I will come and heal him. The Centurian answered and said, Lord, I am not worthy that Thou shouldst come under my roof, but speak the word only and my servant shall be healed. For I am a man under authority, having soldiers under me, and I say unto this man, go and he goeth, and to another, come and he cometh, and to my servant, do and he doeth. When Jesus heard it, He marveled, and said to them that followed, Verily I say unto you, I have not found so great faith, no, not in Israel. And I say unto you that many shall come from the East and West, and shall sit down with Abraham and Isaac and Jacob, in the Kingdom of Heaven."

Jesus, in this case, was able to cure the Centurian's servant with faith, namely the Centurian's faith, for the Centurian had great faith in himself as a man of authority, having many soldiers under him and being able to command them and knowing that his orders would be obeyed. Furthermore, the servant also had great faith in the Centurian's ability and believed and obeyed him. Still further, the Centurian also had great faith in Jesus, as evidenced by his statement that, although he was a man of great authority, he nevertheless said, "Lord, I am not worthy that Thou shouldst come under my roof, but speak the word only, and my servant should be healed." This showed his humbleness to the Lord, and thereby his faith in the Lord's ability to heal by suggestion. In the thirteenth verse, after his prediction regarding the children of the Kingdom, Jesus said unto the Centurian: "Go thy way; and as thou hast believed so be it done unto thee." And his servant was healed in the selfsame hour. It is interesting that Jesus did not say the servant "will be healed." He said, "*as thou hast believed,*" then, "so be it done unto thee," which is an entirely different way of saying it. It was a way Christ had of letting the Centurian realize that his own belief was essential to the curing of his servant. Later on we will see that utilizing faith in the treatment of illness simply permeates the writings of Saint Matthew.

Continuing in Chapter 8, Verses 14 and 15, Jesus cured Peter's mother-in-law of a fever with faith: "And when Jesus was come into Peter's house, He saw his wife's mother laid and sick of a fever, and He touched her hand and the fever left her; and she arose and ministered unto them." Jesus went on curing by direct suggestion as related in Verse 16, which states: "When the even was come, they brought unto Him many that were possessed with devils," (obviously many persons suffering from mental illness) "and He cast out the spirits with His *word*." This is merely another way of saying that something was definitely suggested by word of mouth to each individual patient, and in this way Jesus healed all that were sick. He did not merely modify their illnesses. He cured them. He did not tranquilize them. He made them well. Even the transference of an illness from a patient to the physician, which is a basic principle of some of the methods of hypnotic and psychiatric care today, is seen 2,000 years ago by the genius of physicians, Jesus Christ, when in St. Matthew Chapter 8, Verse 17 it states: "Himself took our infirmities and bare *our* sicknesses."

In Verses 23 through 26, Jesus was able to test the faith of His disciples. "And when He was entered into a ship, His disciples followed Him. And, behold there arose a great tempest in the sea, insomuch that the ship was covered with the waves: but He was asleep. And His disciples came to Him, and awoke Him saying, Lord, save us: we perish. And He saith unto them, Why are ye fearful, O ye of little faith? Then He arose, and rebuked the winds and the sea; and there was a great calm." Again, Jesus realized that, as Dr. Van Pelt has said so often, when emotion enters the door, reason flies out the window, and that with adequate faith one need not be fearful, regardless of external conditions or stimuli.

In the 9th chapter of Matthew, Verses 2 and 3, Jesus heals a palsied man by means of the spoken word. Verse 2 states: "And, behold, they brought to Him a man sick of the palsy, lying on a bed: and Jesus seeing their faith, said unto the sick of the palsy; Son, be of good cheer; thy sins be forgiven thee." Jesus continued to heal many more persons with his *word*, the accounts of which are recorded many times throughout the *New Testament*.

Even in the *Old Testament*, a number of Dr. Van Pelt's statements regarding hypnotic suggestions were in effect, summarized. Dr. Van Pelt has stated that a good hypnotic suggestion must be the right hypnotic suggestion for the individual patient involved; that hypnotic suggestion must be tailor-made and fitted to the individual case, directly utilized at the proper time to achieve the best possible results. Proverbs 25:11 states this maxim of hypno-therapy in these words: "A word fitly spoken is like apples of gold and pictures of silver."

In The Acts, Chapter 19, Verses 1 through 6, Paul is at Ephesus, and having found certain disciples, he called them together to ask them if they had received the Holy Ghost. This was another way of ascertaining (although they intellectually had received Christ as their Savior) whether or not they had experienced the great emotional awakening within their subconscious minds, which he termed "receiving of the Holy Spirit." This was accomplished by the "laying on of hands." This hypnotic technique of influencing the patient to an emotional experience, by means of the sense of touch, has been known to hypnotists long before the time during which Mesmer made such great use of it in his clinic in Paris. Let us read the descriptive verses in the Bible to see how this applies:

"And it came to pass, that, while Apollos was at Corinth, Paul having passed through the upper coasts came to Ephesus: and finding certain disciples, he said unto them, Have ye received the Holy Ghost since ye believed? And they said unto him, We have not so much as heard whether there be any Holy Ghost.' And he said unto them, Unto what then were ye baptized? And they said, Unto John's baptism. Then said Paul, John verily baptized with the baptism of repentance, saying unto the people, that they should believe on Him which should come after him, that is, on Christ Jesus. When they heard this, they were baptized in the name of the Lord Jesus. And when Paul had laid his hands upon them, the Holy Ghost came on them; and they spake with tongues, and prophesied." The hypnotic application of the sense of touch thereby converted an intellectual experience into an emotional one.

While we know that it is certainly easier to learn a foreign language through hypnotic techniques, we also know that by no method known to medical science at present can one learn a complete foreign language in a few minutes, nor can we speak in one language and be heard by our audience in another (except of course through the magic of IBM translators). This nevertheless happened and is recorded in the Bible. It remains as one of the great miracles left to be unravelled as, in time, the good Lord may permit us to do, by understanding more and more of the methods by which He has performed so many wondrous things. The passage clearly states that it was the "laying on of hands" that brought about the great emotional awakening of the subconscious mind which they called "the appearance of the Holy Ghost."

In Matthew, Chapter 9, Verses 20 to 22 it states: "And, behold, a woman, which was diseased with an issue of blood twelve years, came behind him, and touched the hem of his garment: For she said within herself, If I may but touch his garment, I shall be whole. But Jesus turned Him about, and when He saw her, He said, Daughter, be of good comfort; thy faith hath made thee whole. And the woman was made whole from that hour." (Also see Mark 5:25.)

This particular passage illustrates several things. In the first place, it illustrates a case of severe and chronic menorrhagia and metrorrhagia, which had existed for a period of at least twelve years which was rapidly cured through faith. It illustrates the fact that hypnotic suggestion and techniques are perfectly able to cure patients who have been ill for long periods of time, and that the duration of an illness is not the only criteria by which we judge whether an illness is susceptible or is not susceptible to hypnotic treatment. Secondly, this case illustrates excellently the use of auto-suggestion; *e. g.,* the woman *"said within herself,"* which is definitely an example of auto-suggestion, and this has never been seriously disputed by any theological scholar. Her auto-suggestion was that if she might but touch the garment of Jesus she would be made whole; but Jesus, realizing the psychological mechanism operating here, said that she need not worry and that she could be of good comfort since it was not the touching of the garment that made her whole, but the auto-suggestion. In other words, it *was* the faith that made her whole.

This particular point was made very clear by Jesus Himself, and should be an indication to all Biblical scholars that Jesus Himself fully understood the exact mechanism of every method of healing which He used, knowing full well the power, the advantages and disadvantages of all such methods. There is also evidence that He understood the psychopathology which had apparently caused the hormonal imbalance responsible for the twelve years of intermittent bleeding.

In Matthew, Chapter 9, Verses 28 and 29, two blind men came to Jesus and cried: "Thou Son of David, have mercy on us. . . . and Jesus saith unto them, Believe Ye that I am able to do this? They said unto him, Yea, Lord. Then touched He their eyes saying, According to your faith be it unto you. And their eyes were opened . . ."

Again, this particular set of verses illustrates that Jesus invariably asked the patient if *they* felt *they* had the faith that He was able to do this. And even after they replied in the affirmative, His words were always directed thus; "according to your *faith* be it unto you." In this way the door was always open, so that if the faith was not great enough, the man would not be healed. This meant that in each and every case the *patient* had to do *his* part in cooperating with Christ in order for Christ to heal. This is also true of the medical hypnotists, for the patient who has no faith in him and does not cooperate with him will not be healed by him.

In Chapter 9 Verse 32, a dumb man was possessed with the devil, and when the devil was cast out, the dumb man spake, and such psychologically caused speech difficulties are well known in medicine today. Hypnosis is certainly indicated today in the treatment of asphasia, and/or aphonia, which is functional in origin.

The real proof, however, that Jesus needed the cooperation of his patients is given to us in Matthew, Chapter 13,
Verses 57 and 58, which state: "And they were offended in
Him. But Jesus said unto them, A prophet is not without honor,
save in his own country and in his own house. And He did not
many mighty works there because of their unbelief."

This illustrated how Jesus, when he returned to His own
home in Nazareth, was rejected by His own people and neighbors. Nowadays we still see evidence of the fact that we feel
it impossible to believe that an expert, on any subject, exists
in our own locality and hence we often travel far afield to
search out the experts in any given field. Since the use of
hypnotic techniques with which Jesus had chosen to do His
healing depended largely on the faith of the patient, Jesus
was not able to do "many mighty works" in his own home town,
because of their unbelief.

In the 14th Chapter of Matthew, Verses 25 through 31
it states: "And in the fourth watch of the night Jesus went
unto them, walking on the sea. And when the disciples saw
Him walking on the sea, they were troubled, saying, It is a
spirit; and they cried out for fear. But straightway Jesus spake
unto them, saying, Be of good cheer; it is I; be not afraid. And
Peter answered Him and said, Lord, if it be Thou, bid me come
unto Thee on the water. And He said Come. And when Peter
was come down out of the ship, he walked on the water, to
go to Jesus. But when he saw the wind boisterous, he was
afraid; and beginning to sink, he cried, saying, Lord, save me.
And immediately Jesus stretched forth His hand, and caught
him, and said unto him, O thou of little faith, wherefore didst
thou doubt?" In this miraculous incident, where Jesus and Peter
walked on the water, we see that the action of fear in Peter
produced tenseness, in the same manner that it produces pain
in our patients undergoing hypnotic anesthesia. Although
Jesus, through the powers of his great mind, was able to walk
on the water and "be not afraid," Peter became afraid when
the wind became boisterous and he naturally began to sink.

The Lord, however, pulled him up, illustrating the ability of faith to perform miracles.

The real power of Christ was demonstrated by His use of the many powerful hypnotic techniques at his disposal. This is well-illustrated throughout the Book of Matthew, another example of which is found in Chapter 17, Verses 14 through 20: "And when they were come to the multitude, there came to Him a certain man, kneeling down to Him, and saying, Lord, have mercy on my son, for he is a lunatick and sore vexed, for ofttimes he falleth into the fire, and oft into the water, and I have brought him to Thy disciples, and they could not cure him. Then Jesus answered and said, O faithless and perverse generation, how long shall I be with you? How long shall I suffer you? Bring him hither to me. And Jesus rebuked the devil, and he departed out of him, and the child was cured from that very hour. Then came the disciples to Jesus apart, and said, Why could not we cast him out? and Jesus said unto them, Because of your unbelief, for verily I say unto you, if ye have faith as a grain of mustard seed, ye shall say unto this mountain, Remove hence to yonder place; and it shall remove; and nothing shall be impossible unto you."

It is important to experience the creativity of faith. Hypnosis enables us to concentrate our minds in such a fashion as to produce faith, which in turn is the instrument by which we create the thing or things in which we have faith.

"Thou shalt also decree a thing, and it shall be established unto thee; and the light shall shine on thy ways." (Job 22:28.)

Jesus even predicted the advancement of medical science to the point that courses in hypno-therapy would be given to physicians and dentists, and that they themselves would carry on the good work which Christ had begun when he said, "Verily, Verily I say unto you, He that believeth on me, the works that I do, shall he do also, and *greater works than these shall he do.*" There is no limit to the good which we as physicians can do for mankind if we simply have the courage to exercize our faith.

Chapter VI

THE USE OF RELIGIOUS
PRINCIPLES IN HYPNO-ANALYSIS

PART 1. AN AID TO INDUCTION

One of the difficulties encountered in the practice of hypno-analysis is the proper induction of the subject. While induction into a light trance of hypnosis is generally not difficult, it is sometimes difficult to induce the emotional experience necessary to obtain the proper catharsis, which is needed to bring about the patient's recovery. Those persons capable of easily experiencing and expressing their emotions are frequently the targets for emotional illness, and consequently are also the best subjects. Occasionally, however, we are faced with a stoic person whose personality because of its inflexibility is difficult to stir into emotional activity. This type of individual generally does not suffer from emotional illness; but in the event that he does need therapy, he may become a particular problem to the physician who is entrusted with his care. One of the blessings of treating this type of individual is that should his inflexible personality and firm convictions have a religious basis, these beliefs can then be used to great advantage both in analysis and in psychosynthesis following analysis. An example of this follows:

In one particular case of a sixty-seven year old woman, it was necessary to produce hypnoanesthesia for a particular operative procedure. The patient concentrated only poorly, and was unable to visualize to any great extent. She was mentally taken for a walk in the woods, a trip to the seashore, and to various other situations in which it was hoped that she would be able to concentrate her mind sufficiently to produce the desired anesthesia. None of these however were successful until I stumbled onto the idea of using the woman's firm religious convictions as a method for visualization. Although she was unable to visualize the trees in the forest, the waves of the ocean, or a circle on a blackboard, when told that she would be able to visualize the angels standing at the top of a long white marble staircase, and that step by step she would climb the staircase, she immediately hallucinated the desired objects, placed herself in the situation completely, and produced a perfect anesthesia.

In a similar case a patient who had little faith in his "doctors" yet had a great deal of faith in the Lord, was persuaded through the use of hypnosis that the Lord, not his "doctors," would produce the desired anesthesia. Since he was firmly convinced that the Lord never failed, the anesthesia obviously didn't fail either.

The two previous examples therefore illustrate rather well how persons with firm religious convictions may be aided in their induction or in their production of anesthesia. The mere repetition of the direct suggestion that God's grace is sufficient for all the patient's needs is frequently a great help in alleviating pre-operative or pre-analytic fears. Similar passages from the Bible which are helpful in reducing the apprehension of patients, which so often retards their progress, are: "Be strong and of good courage, fear not nor be afraid of them; for the Lord thy God, He is it that doth go with thee; He will not fail thee nor forsake thee" (Deuteronomy 31:6). "Fear not, for I am with thee" (Isaiah 43:5). "I will not fail thee nor forsake thee" (Joshua 1:5). For those persons who have a deep religious conviction and even more important an unshakable faith in the strength and power of God to help them, will progress rapidly towards the solution of their problem in a cure of their illness, provided religious principles are utilized while the patient is in the hypnotic trance. (Second Samuel Chapter 22:29 through 33) "For thou art my lamp, oh Lord, and the Lord will lighten my darkness. For by thee I have run through a troop: by my God have I leaped over a wall. As for God, his way is perfect;

the word of the Lord is tried, He is a buckler to all them that trust in Him. For who is God, save the Lord? and who is a rock, save our God? God is my strength and power: and he maketh my way perfect."

A patient who accepts this philosophy at a subconscious level is certainly unlikely to secrete excess adrenalin either immediately prior to surgery or to analysis. Hence, during surgery we are missing the adrenalin effect of dilating the superficial blood vessels which is responsible for so much excess bleeding. Both in surgery and in analysis we are missing the high blood pressure and high pulse rate which are also generated by adrenalin and other like compounds which are secreted in response to fear.

PART 2. THE FATHER FIGURE

The search for, misinterpretation of, and confusion about the father figure is responsible for a great deal of mental illness. Indeed, the absence of a father figure can certainly lead to dire consequences, especially when this is related to God. One case comes to mind of a sixteen year old girl who had been a juvenile delinquent being involved with the authorities on charges of drunkeness, lewd conduct, and petty theft. She was also a truant from school and indeed on occasion would leave school for periods of months at a time. Her mother, a strict Morman, had no real understanding of the girl's problem and subconsciously rejected her. Indeed, the more the young girl got into trouble, the more her mother used these incidents to produce a certain martyrdom for herself. The girl's father had died at an early age from an accident, and the girl's subconscious resentment of a loss of her father figure, plus her hostility to her mother because of the obvious parental rejection she received, carried her from bad to worse. In searching for a father figure, she would attempt sometimes successfully and sometimes unsuccessfully to seduce older men, and then upon completion of this real or fancied intercourse, she would develop great feelings of guilt because she subconsciously connected these men with her own father. Analysis and subsequent synthesis reassured her that although she had experienced the loss of her human father, that she still was in full possession of her heavenly father who was just as real and a great deal more reliable. She immediately began to improve. She returned to school, and her school work improved rapidly. She entered into school activities and her reputation with her fellow students gradually began to change. No longer regarded as the class prostitute, but as an ambitious young lady attempting to straighten out her life, she soon won the admiration of her teachers and her schoolmates. Indeed, the decreased amount of expression of her hostility for her mother caused some difficulty since the mother could no longer use this to fulfill her own psychopathological needs. Although quite "religious" for a good many years, her mother had nevertheless not experienced the rebirth in Christ so necessary to the follower of the Christian religion. Her anxieties eventually, however, led her into an Evangelical meeting, where for the first time she experienced the "emotional rebirth" and began to obtain some insight into her own behavior. Although their problems are far from over, both mother and daughter are learning to understand themselves in an objective and self assured manner, born of the trust and faith which they have duly received. In the young girl's case, her decision for Christ was directly brought about through the use of hypno-analysis, by placing her in a frame of mind in which she could accept the father figure for which she sought so desperately. In the mother's case, a decision was brought about at an Evangelical meeting. These two cases in the same family illustrate nicely the parallel between some aspects of hypnosis in religion.

To illustrate the difficulty and anxiety which can be caused by the absence of a father figure altogether, let us review the case of Mr. E. N. Mr. E. N. is a fifty-eight year old white male, an acute asthmatic, who came to me with the following complaint: "I am a lame-brain with a psychosomatic overlay on every situation that arises. No matter what it is I end up suffocating from emphysema or asthma. I break out into a sweat, I start to suffocate, and I go into a panic. I only have two outs. The first one is my intermittent positive pressure breathing apparatus which is at home, and the second one is an adrenalin injection. These two outs are the only things that keep me alive. As a boy—until I was eleven years old—I had bronchial asthma. If I had even tipped over in bed, I would have suffocated. I know because my parents said this over and over. At eleven, I moved into the country and that was the end of the asthma. I have been a hard working mechanic all my life, but I remember the doctors told my parents, and my parents chatted to the neighbors that I couldn't possibly live past eleven years old. Once I did live past eleven then my asthma was gone. Six years ago though we had a 45 ft. cabin cruiser boat, and I had an emotional upset on it. I had a few drinks, lay down to sleep, and when I woke up I couldn't breathe, and I have had my asthma ever since. I've had this for six years, but the panic is becoming more acute as every day goes by. I have taken a number of tranquilizers and they help temporarily. The best drug I have ever taken was Librium, but even that doesn't solve the problem. I know that if I could just control my emotions, I could breathe. I have seen any number of psychiatrists, and been in and out of hospitals, but I seem to continue to get worse."

When asked about his occupation he stated, "I am a mechanic, and one of the best in the business, but I've really never liked it." When asked what he would rather do he stated, "Exactly what you are doing." He was then questioned on his married life and stated that he had been very happy for the past seventeen years during which he was married to his present wife. They had had many misunderstandings because of his wife's mother, whom the patient states he cannot forgive, but he describes his wife as a "sweet rose," who unfortunately has a terrific mother complex which tears the patient to pieces. He states his first wife walked out with the postman, and even had the nerve to sell me my own car back.

He had to pay for both divorces but his wife committed suicide later, which he said "didn't bother me one bit." When asked about his religious affiliation he stated he was Protestant and had been a member of the Unity, Christian Science, Methodist, Presbyterian, and a number of other churches. He said he was also three years as a Yoga and had belonged to various sects but "never found the answer." He neither drinks nor smokes and had been placed on Librium and Miltown medication for his asthma. He also states that it is impossible for him to sleep, and that he hasn't had a good night's sleep without barbituates in years. He has an eight year old daughter whom he idolizes and his wife has two grown boys, one by her former husband and one adopted by the patient, and his first wife. He lived mortally in fear that some physician would give him Sodium Pentathol which he had been told by a doctor is extremely dangerous for emphysema.

The rest of his past history was essentially negative except for a heart murmur which he stated was a result of a previous attack of rheumatic fever as a child. Describing his childhood he stated, "it was normal," but his father and mother were divorced when he was eighteen years old. He described his father as one of the most level-headed, finest persons he had ever known in his life, and "everybody loved him." He described his mother as "a bundle of dynamite, the same as my wife." Apparently his father brought a boarder to live in the house who eventually became sexually involved with the patient's mother. The patient knew it and tried to inform his father about what was going on between his mother and the boarder. This led to some deep traumatic psychological experiences. He also had some unpleasant experiences in school when his teacher used to beat him. He became apprehensive about surgery and physicians, because he was a boxer and had had many injuries. His sexual life was essentially normal.

One other damaging incident in his past was when he ran into an old man with his car, as the man stepped out of a safety zone. The patient stated the old man actually jumped in front of his car, but the police held the patient for homicide. Finally, the old man awoke and said it was his fault, and two witnesses also confirmed the story so the patient was released. The patient obviously had a very depressed ego, and was punishing himself and his wife. Even at the first consultation period it was easy to see that his early childhood asthma had a sensitizing effect, and that something happened to him six years ago which started the incident all over again. To summarize, his asthma and insomnia seemed to be his main presenting symptoms, but as is so often the case, the presenting symptoms do not indicate the cause of the problem. Indeed, most frequently the cause of a given psychosomatic illness has nothing to do with the presenting symptoms in an ordinary or rational sense.

It was realized that because of his symptoms beginning on a boat, it might be unwise to use a beach visualization scene to hypnotize him. Accordingly, a different method was employed. After induction he was given a long and involved word association test, which was extremely revealing. Without going into the details of the test, the results obtained under hypnosis clearly showed that he was extremely hostile to his mother and father for breaking up their home, and also for planting the ideas into his head at an early age that he could not possibly live past eleven. Realizing this was a good deal of the cause for his first asthma, he developed a tremendous hostility for his parents. In reality this hostility was also in part for himself, for even as a child, he had the hostility for his parents and expressed it to them by informing his father on the sexual activities of his mother. This caused him to develop such terrible guilt feelings (namely that he was himself responsible for the breaking up of his own family) that he felt an overwhelming need for self punishment. The only way to punish himself in this fashion was to cripple himself up with asthma, for this also was a means to protect himself from carrying out any of his more violent thoughts. This was the basis of the analysis on the first level.

When a deeper level was penetrated, which was extremely difficult with this patient and was done only with the combination of hypnosis and trilene, the patient went into a narcosis and kept repeating in a rapid machine-gun fashion the words "I am dead" "I am dead" "I am dead," over and over hundreds of times. The real horrible pathology of this patient was that his mind had actually accepted the idea that he was already dead. Indeed, he was a walking zombie, and he was extremely hostile and angry at the anesthetist for having "killed" him. This "occurred" when he was eleven years old. He had already had his initial sensitizing event in early life, at which time his parents had unwittingly planted in his mind the seed that he could never live past eleven.

He remembered an incident under hypnosis when he was eleven years old. He was involved in a bicycle accident which caused a broken arm, and he had to have it set. At the time the anesthetist was lowering the mask over his face, the patient accepted the thought that he was actually dying, and did in fact mentally "die" from that point on. It was for this reason that his asthma cleared up, as obviously "dead men do not have asthma." It was only because he woke up on the boat some many years later and realized that he was in fact still alive that he, therefore, had to suffocate from his asthma again, and it became tremendously worse.

At the deepest part of his analysis, it was finally determined that the person to whom he expressed the greatest hostility was neither his mother, his father, the anesthetist, nor even himself. He really hated God, something he could not even admit to himself. He had accepted the idea that God was responsible for his suffering, and truly hated him. Because of this horrible thought, and this of course was entirely on a subconscious level, he felt that he had to atone constantly for his sins, and even said "I believe I am following my 'soul pattern' paying for the errors, mistakes, and sins which I committed in a previous life." The previous life was in reality his life up until age eleven. He then expressed many unusual religious beliefs including reincarnation, but blamed himself and God for his own "faulty" creation, steeping himself further in guilt and becoming sicker and sicker.

He finally began to improve only when he was made to see by an advanced hypno-analytic method that he did not have the right to judge himself. During the process of a deep emotional experience the biblical quotation of Matthew Chapter 7, verse 1 "Judge not that ye be not judged" was brought to his attention in the fashion that he not only did not have the right to judge himself and that if he was judging himself he was usurping the dominion of God.

Once he accepted the fact that only God could judge him and that his sins therefore could not be expiated by punishing himself, but only by laying the entire load on God's grace through Christ he finally began to improve. Later after realizing the miracle of grace and the importance of God's gift through Christ's redemption of his sins, the man was also able to change his hate to love. It was at this point in his therapy that he experienced his greatest advancement. It was unfortunate that the man had gone through over six years of incredible physical torture which he had placed upon himself in the belief that he could expiate himself from his guilt feelings through the means of self-punishment. He had been literally suffocating himself to death.

This case dramatically illustrates how a negative attitude toward God can easily be introduced and accepted by the unwary mind and cause a great deal of physical illness, which though treated adequately by modern medical means, nevertheless, fails to respond until the root cause is ferreted out through the correct application of religious principles during analysis under hypnosis.

Still a different problem is illustrated by the following case in which the patient's illness was actually caused by a misinterpretation by him of an Evangelical sermon given by a Catholic priest. This case illustrated a number of interesting points. Not the least of these is the point that the audience in church is frequently in and out of the state of hypnosis and that great good can be done by the placement of positive suggestions in the subconscious minds of those listening intently and concentrating upon the sermon. However, a sermon which misdirects or which concentrates upon the negative aspect, or which tends to frighten rather than comfort, may actually introduce anxiety into the listener which later pops out as a full-fledged neurosis. For this reason all ministers should be extremely careful regarding content and delivery of their sermons, and examine sermons with the utmost meticulousness in order to make sure that their sermons achieve the purpose for which they were designed.

Following is the case of Mr. R. M., a successful Italian business man who first came to me with the problem of fear neurosis. The unfortunate patient was afraid of almost everything. His scope of activities was limited geographically to a small area near his home, and he was afraid whenever he had to leave this area. He even carried a bottle of smelling salts in his pocket for years for fear he might faint. He became so nervous and extremely limited in his work that he had to seek help, and had seen not only five psychiatrists but another well-known hypnotist with no results.

It was obvious that no one had reached the root cause of his problem. Most of all the patient feared death. He could not enter a movie theater; he could not go to church for fear of death. He could not go to any funerals, drive down certain streets, enter into any house where anyone he had known had passed away, and many other behavior patterns made life increasingly difficult for him. Unlike the previous patient who actually accepted the idea that he was dead, this patient was obsessed with the fear of dying.

The time the initial sensitizing event occurred was when the patient was forced by his parents to attend a church mission. He was in High School at the time and the sermon involved was on death. Instead of orienting the sermon to the theme of eternal life, the priest had unfortunately preached only on the negative aspect of death. He repeated the words time after time frightening the patient, stating over and over that anyone in the congregation might be dead next year, next month, next week, the next day, the next hour or even the next minute. The message became so frightening to the patient that he became deathly nauseated, had to leave the church and became quite sick, vomiting violently. His subconscious mind had obviously accepted the negative thoughts and the patient simply could not stomach them.

From that moment on the patient developed one illness after another. He was diagnosed as having gastro-enteritis, ulcers, etc. He had many gastro-intestinal x-rays and saw many specialists, all to no avail. During the war, he entered the service as a volunteer Officer Cadet, and although he became an excellent pilot his terrible fears prevented him from continuing in that occupation.

His worst attack of fear occurred when he was driving to a hospital at which his sister-in-law was having a baby. The reason for this attack was revealed later under analysis as being the fact that his grandfather died in a hospital. He described his attacks of fear as the "exact same feeling you would get from an automobile accident." The patient had had an unhappy childhood largely due to the fact that as an Italian he was discriminated against in his community, and also due to the fact that his mother was constantly ill from psychoneurotic causes. He was forced to work when very young and never weighed over 120 pounds until he was married. He had to quit school in the ninth grade and had resented it ever since.

The worst effect of all of his background was the effect that it had on his subconscious mind in depreciating his ego. Not only had "God" let him down by prescribing death at every turn in life's road, but the patient truly felt himself to be an inferior individual because of the constant depreciation which was due to his earlier background of poverty in Italian immigrant status. With psychosynthetic hypnotic techniques the patient was made to realize that as an American, he was a citizen of the most advanced country in the world, and that as an Italian-American he was privileged to have the background of a nation that has been more responsible for the development of our law, medicine, language, and general conduct of life than any other nation in the world. The patient was able to develop a pride in himself and *believe* it on an emotional level, which he was unable to do before.

Once he was age-regressed back to the various incidents which caused his fear and made to see that each one of these was fearful only because it was connected with the previous illness or death, he began to lose his fears. After ridding himself of his hostility towards his parents by building a protective wall around himself through which they could no longer penetrate, he became more relaxed and tranquil. His biggest improvement naturally occurred when he was able to realize the existence of and remove the hypnotic suggestion planted in his mind unintentionally by the well-meaning priest.

When the patient realized that the priest's message had actually been a message of eternal life rather than one of death, his entire attitude changed; and, analytically realizing this on an emotional level, he has begun to *act* on these beliefs in a positive fashion. To date every single one of his fears has been removed. He has stopped all medication including sleeping pills and tranquilizers which he formerly had to take daily in large doses. He now drives alone, something he could never do before, ventures out into territories which formerly he could not do. He has entered the supermarket on the corner near his home even though a man had been shot dead there some time ago, and he has walked across the street to a house in which a man died, a house which he was formerly unable to enter. He can even go to a theater and sit in a seat which is not on the aisle and feel comfortable throughout the entire performance, which was simply unthinkable before his hypno-analytic therapy. Indeed, he is completely well except for the fact that he has not yet returned to church. After a few more sessions of hypno-therapy there is no doubt in my mind but what this obstacle will be overcome, and the patient will experience a complete cure.

A very fascinating case, completely different from any of the previous ones does not concern either the absence of God or the misconception of God, but rather a confusion about who is God. This is the case of a lawyer, Mr. K. R., who was extremely fearful because he was becoming a "pill addict." He depended upon tranquilizers and medications more and more to maintain his equilibrium and sleep. He was subject to severe migraine and tension headaches which he could remember as far back as his childhood. He realized his situation was as he reported to me "calm on the outside and hell on the inside." The patient most of all had difficulty in going to sleep and a tremendous fear of going to bed. Even if "dead tired," he would fall asleep for a short while, but then wake up again at 2 a.m. and was through for the night. When sunlight came in, however, he could fall asleep nicely. This is not an unusual complaint and is generally associated with a subconscious reason or hypnotic suggestion which the patient under such circumstances feels he has to be awake to be on guard against some mythical danger which his mind perceives to be present. Since the mind cannot distinguish between a real danger and an imagined one, and since it has accepted the hypnotic suggestion that a danger really exists, the patient is kept awake constantly to remain on guard against this mythical danger.

The patient realized he was running away from himself and blamed a good deal of his difficulty on his family problems, since he was the sole support of his present family, a previous wife and two children, and his own mother and father. The financial burden was staggering but this was not the root cause of his trouble, as was soon found out under analysis. Hypno-analysis was done by a very rapid type of treatment designed to specifically reach the root cause in the shortest possible time obviating the necessity for long hours of psychoanalytic work on the couch. Analysis which is not directed leads only to confusion. Obviously the analysis in this case had to be directed toward the cause of his insomnia. This patient indeed had been under psycho-analysis for five years, with no positive results whatsoever. However, in less than half a dozen treatments under the rapid analysis the man was totally well.

By exploring traumatic incidents in the patient's past, he vividly revealed to himself an incident describing his mother's death, a violent death in which his mother was hit on the head accidentally by a blunt object. Age-regressing the patient before this death, it was noted that the mother had frequently said to the patient that he was the cause of her frequent migraine headaches. In a small way then the patient subconsciously blamed himself for his mother's death, even though he in no way had to do with the skull fracture caused by the accidental blow to her head. Indeed, he began to build up such guilt feelings regarding this, that he felt the necessity to keep his mother alive. He did this in a number of ways. The first way was to idolize her as a God. She could do no wrong in his eyes and would live "forever" in his memory. However, it was found out that he had even adopted certain characteristics of his mother in order to keep her alive within his body.

This was brought out on a deep level during the word association test under analysis during which he associated his father with a merchant, then immediately said, "I am not a merchant." This really indicated that he was saying quite positively that he was not his father; since there was no reason for him to deny that fact, one can only assume that therefore he was his mother, and this certainly proved to be the fact.

When the patient had lost his mother, he stated that for a long time he did not believe in God. This came about as a result of an uncle who told him at the time of his mother's death that his family had been so happy with his mother that God in his loneliness had borrowed his mother. Although the uncle's intentions had been good, he had set up in the patient's subconscious mind a situation in which God had become a source of competition for his mother's love. This allowed the patient to hate God. Such hate naturally brought on deep guilt feelings on his part and these guilt feelings in turn demanded punishment. Instead, he changed God into mother and placed both within himself.

Under hypno-analysis, the reason finally manifested itself showing the patient why he felt the need to stay awake, on guard to protect the mother within him. Once he was able to dissociate mother from God, he realized that she was not a diety and in fact a human, a human who died, a human who did not need to be kept alive by himself, who indeed had eternal life through God, and who did not need to be guarded. Once the confusion had cleared away regarding the diety and the patient realized in fact that his own mother was not God, and that God in fact was omnipotent and not a lowly competitor for his mother's affections, then he was not only able to cure his insomnia, but also he was able to develop a new outlook on life which permitted him a greater peace of mind and tranquility than he had ever known previously in his entire existence. Now, leading a life of quiet trust, the patient goes about his professional business with the calm self-assurance of one who walks with God.

In these brief case histories then, we have been able to illustrate various methods by which religious principles may be used in the practice of hypno-analysis, as well as pointing out that faults and misconceptions regarding religion can also be a great source of mental disease which can best be ferreted out through the use of hypnosis and treated by means of a thorough understanding on an emotional level of the principles of a loving, benevolent God who, through His grace, grants us eternal salvation.

Chapter VII

THE SEARCH FOR GOD

I hope this particular chapter will help to explain some of the connections between hypnosis and religion, and emphasize the direct relationship between theology and hypnosis. In the first place, when we are searching for anything, we are by the very nature of the word exploring various pathways which we hope will lead us to a definite goal. In the case of communion with God, there are three pathways which lead to this same goal. The first pathway is through the pathway of ultimate knowledge or through the head; the second pathway is the pathway through ultimate love or through the heart; and the third is the pathway of ultimate service or through the hands. By any one of these pathways one can find and get to know the Deity for, if one has ultimate knowledge, one recognizes the need for love and service, if one has ultimate love one has at the same time great knowledge and recognizes the need for service; and if one devotes one's life to service to others, one already has attained the ultimate knowledge and brotherly love necessary to reach the Deity. Therefore, this pinnacle upon which the Deity rests is a three-sided mountain with a precipitous climb, regardless of which pathway is selected. The top of this mountain is as "a razor's edge," the razor's edge to which that great physician-writer, W. Somerset Maugham, referred to in his book of the same name, published some years ago.

In all three cases God is *within you*. We have many proofs of this: Ephesians, 4:6 "One God and Father, who is above all, and through all, and *IN* you all." Paul tells us, "Know ye not that ye are the temple of God and that the Spirit of God dwelleth *in* you?" (Paraphrased Corinthians 6:19.) Indeed, if there is to be any force for good in our lives it must come from within us in order that it should influence the sincerity of our actions toward the world without.

Since God lies within us, it should be axiomatic that our search for God must begin within ourselves. In other words we find God not only by the "scientific" investigation of the outer world, but by "hypnotic" metaphysical investigation of the inner spiritual world as well. One of the difficulties which has presented itself through the years, with regard to biblical interpretation and proof, has been that so many persons in the study of spiritual phenomena have tried to prove them by the scientific methods and logic by which we prove the physical phenomena which exist on the earth. It follows then, however, that scientific phenomena are proved by the scientific method. Spiritual phenomena however, are proved by the hypnotic or spiritual method, frequently in conjunction with scientific controls.

It is necessary, therefore, for us to know how to make contact with our subconscious minds in order to contact the God which is within us. The hypnotic methods for contacting our subconscious mind have already been explained in other volumes, and the similarities between hypnosis and prayer have already been discussed. Furthermore, the relationship between the mind and soul, both being psycho-philosophical units rather than anatomical ones, makes it important that we are properly attuned spiritually in order to make contact with the God that is present within us. Here are four ways in which this can be done:

The first way is through sincere faith. Abraham was a symbol of faith, as is illustrated by all of Chapter 22 of Genesis. John Greenleaf Whittier in his poem *The Eternal Goodness* expressed his spirit of faith, saying "I know not what the future hath of marvel or surprise, assured alone that life and death His mercy underlies." And "I know not where His islands lift their fronded palms in air; I only know I cannot drift beyond His love and care."

Elizabeth York Case in her poem, *There Is No Unbelief,* states: "The heart lives by that faith the lips deny. God knoweth why!" Arthur Guterman's poem, *In the Hospital,* speaks of faith as a method by which to reach God when he says, "Passion and tenderness aid me, I know there is God."

The second method through which we contact the God within us is by allowing the God that is within us to control our thoughts, which in turn control our bodily processes. Man may either build or tear down his physical being with his thoughts, and pro-survival thinking begets survival, just as sure as anti-survival thinking brings on death. Dr. Van Pelt noted that the main threats to longevity now are the so-called psychosomatic "stress" diseases. He also pointed out that persons who lived to be over one hundred had only one factor in common, *their state of mind.* They all enjoyed life, took a real interest in living and wanted to go on doing so. Dr. Van Pelt[6] states:

"Modern research reveals that hypnosis is only a super-concentrated state of mind. It may be brought about by suggestion, direct or indirect, by the person himself or an operator, deliberately or accidentally.

"In this state of mind suggestion can have far-reaching bodily effects.

"Hypnosis must be regarded in the light of modern research as a normally occuring phenomenon of everyday life.

"The popular idea that it is necessary to be stretched out and unconscious or act like a 'zombie' to be hypnotized is far from the truth.

"In the deepest state of hypnosis the subject can open his eyes, walk about and act in every way as though normal. In fact, he could not be detected as hypnotised by the ordinary person.

"Thus the person with an obsession or compulsion to say, do or think certain things over and over is hypnotised.

6 *How to be 100 by Hypnosis* by Dr. S. J. Van Pelt. British Journal of Medical Hypnotism Vol 9, No. 4, Summer 1958 issue.

"The person suffering from anxiety state 'panic attacks,' depression or psychosomatic disorders as asthma, hay fever or migraine, is hypnotised.

"In fact any psychoneurotic or psychosomatic disorder can be experimentally induced by hypnosis and as easily removed.

"The centenarian is merely a person who is convinced, or obsessed, or hypnotised by the idea that he enjoys life, wants to go on living and will do so to a 100 or more."

The mind can prolong life. Dr. Van Pelt continues by saying: "It is well known that a native will sicken and die of no clinically demonstrable disease if he believes the 'medicine man' or 'witch doctor' has put a curse on him. The native simply hypnotises himself into believing he will die, and so he does.

"Many cases are known where when one old person has died, the companion has lost all will to live and died shortly afterwards.

"On the other hand, the 'will to live' is very strong and has saved many people. Marchesi has described the case of a weak, worn-out old woman of ninety, dying from bilateral broncho-pneumonia. In spite of having no sulpha drugs or penicillin, she recovered because she 'willed' herself to do so to stop her relatives inheriting her money!

Centenarians, having unconsciously hypnotised themselves into a strong desire to live and enjoy life, influence their organs and glands so that they work at maximum efficiency."

During the war many men in prison camps who might have been saved by hypnosis and prayer lost their will to live and died. Living in a physical sense on earth is also comparable to our spiritual life. It must also be constantly fed and nourished if we are to survive spiritually. As Mohammed once said, "If thou hast two loaves of bread, sell one and buy white hyacinths for thy soul." Caswell[7] has spoken eloquently of this by saying:

[7] *New Horizons* by Robert W. Caswell.

"Unless your soul is fed as well as your physical body, your body cannot compensate for the loss that comes from this soul starvation. No amount of material supply will recompense you for the loss of soul satisfaction."

By constantly conditioning our mind to respond with pro-survival reactions and thoughts, we feed both the body and the soul increasing our longevity both physically and spiritually. It is important, therefore, that we constantly maintain ourselves in an atmosphere of positive pro-survival thinking in order to maintain our contact with the God that is within. Since God himself is pro-survival, immortality being one way of surviving, a survival cycle is established which constantly re-energizes the person involved. Similarly anti-survival thinking leads to pain, anxiety, and other undesirable emotions which trigger a vicious cycle which ultimately ends only in death. It is important to stop worrying and start living; living with a trust which more than compensates for the anxieties and stresses of life which are part of our civilization today.

The third method by which we contact the God within us is by allowing God to give our life purpose.

(a) Age is no barrier in this regard, as illustrated by the fact that Moses lead his people after eighty, Henry Ford was poor at forty, Franklin D. Roosevelt had polio after forty, but nevertheless was elected President of the United States for four successive terms, while suffering from the ravages of this dread disease. Lincoln was a failure at fifty, and indeed had turned out poorly. He had been robbed, cheated, and deserted by his friends so that at one time during his life he stated that he was even afraid to carry a pocket-knife with him for fear that he might commit suicide; and yet he went through this trial testing period which was so necessary to develop in him the compassion he was later to display as the greatest President the United States has ever had. Remember that Gaugin started painting after forty and Michaelangelo painted the magnificent and awesome ceiling of the Sistine Chapel, his greatest work after he was eighty years old. Today, thousands of people marvel at these paintings in the Vatican in Rome. Edison did his greatest work after he reached the age of seventy, when his factories and buildings had all burned together with the priceless research documents of a lifetime.

(b) Neither is sex a barrier. All great personages of the world were certainly not men. Women like Florence Nightingale, Madame Curie, Eleanor Roosevelt, Sarah Bernhardt, Jane Adams, Joan of Arc, Betsy Ross, and thousands of others have selflessly given of their time and talents to rise to greatness when they simply allowed God to give their lives purpose, as did Mary the Mother of our Lord.

(c) Education is no barrier either. Abraham Lincoln was self-taught; George Washington Carver began life as a slave; and the disciples of Christ Himself were men of little or moderate education. They rose to greatness when they allowed God to give their life purpose.

(d) Fourthly, color, creed or nationality is no barrier to greatness of character. Ralph Bunch, Hachikawa, Duke Ellington, Mahatma Gandhi, Marion Anderson, Albert Schweitzer, Albert Einstein and many other contemporaries of ours are available for awards of greatness.

The fourth method to contact the God within us is by the use of techniques. (a) A super-relaxation of the body to enable one to devote all of one's energies to the spirit. (b) The super-concentration of the mind and the fixation of the mental vision upon God. (c) The acceptance of the good suggestions which come from this God-like portion of the sub-conscious, immediately and without question, forms the basis for the acceptance of the principle "not my will but Thine be done."

Through the mechanism of these four techniques then, one may contact the subconscious mind, and thereby obtain a relationship between the God that is within us, and thoughts of the thinking part of our mind.

Chapter VIII

THE HYPNOTIC PROOF OF GOD

In previous chapters we have drawn a comparison between the anatomical unit of mass known as the brain, and the unit of energy or power within it known as the mind. Furthermore we have divided the brain anatomically into the cerebrum or thinking part and the lower brain centers housing the store-house of the emotions. The power of the thinking part of the brain or cerebrum is the conscious mind. The power of the lower brain centers, such as the thalamus and hypothalamus, is the subconscious mind. Just as the anatomical units of the brain are composed of units of mass called cells, so is the mind composed of smaller units of energy called "Units of mind power." Through superconcentration of the mind (a form of hypnosis) on the Deity, we are able to accept fully and completely certain facts through Faith, and as we experience this emotional re-birth accepting it as fact it then becomes a reality for us.

For example: we accept the fact that Christ died on the Cross for *our* sins, that we have been cleansed from all unrighteousness because of this. It becomes a reality to us and at that moment, the soul (which is the unit of power corresponding to the anatomical unit of the body) experiences an indwelling of the spirit (power) and grows in size and stature.

The size of our soul can be likened to a balloon small and empty until through the use of hypnosis it is filled by the breath of God which gives it greater and greater power. Its size, therefore, depends on the amount that our soul is filled up with God. It is important therefore to constantly increase the size of our own soul, increasing its power and locating it

69

throughout our entire mental and physical being, in order to obtain maximum action and effect from this great warehouse of goodness.

Through Hypnosis we have proven many times that mind power of phenomenal proportions exists. It seems obvious therefore that with power of this proportion existing in the mind, there must be then a Universal Mind from which all ideas spring and which has communication in some way with our own subconscious processes, since all of us draw a certain amount from its great storehouse of knowledge.

In the same manner we can then prove the existence of God (something scholars and theologians have been trying to do for centuries). If we admit that the soul is a storehouse of spiritual power within us, a storehouse which comes with us when we are born and which leaves us when we die, a storehouse which is given power as our faith comes into being through hypnotic techniques, a storehouse which receives power (God) as our minds become concentrated and hypnotized, obsessed with, and possessed with the acceptance of Christ as our personal Saviour; then by combining this POWER within each of us, which has been given to us by virtue of accepting Him, we have a combination of all soul power, indeed a Universal Soul composed not of mass but of Energy and Power which is God Himself. In this respect and using this concept, it is easy to see why He is not limited by flesh and bones or any other anatomical structure of mass. We know that we cannot drift beyond His Love and Care any more than we can drift beyond the energy and power of the Universe, the power of Goodness that is God.

In the preceeding paragraphs we have attempted to offer a rather clumsy and primitive proof of the existence of the Universal Mind and the Universal Soul on the basis of energy rather than mass. It is easier to prove this through the use of Hypnosis since it is also dependent upon the concentration of energy and is the key to satisfying religious experience whether one calls it by the name of Hypnosis, Mono-Ideaism, Prayer, or by still another name.

If this power within is going to mean anything valuable to us and to the world, then it must be harnessed as the great rivers must be dammed to form electric power for our vast lighting systems. Harnessing Soul-Power depends on two things. First, it must have direction, Divine direction. (Power alone used in the wrong direction is dangerous, indeed destructive). Secondly, it must be turned on and utilized to its full extent through the bodies which we were given for that purpose. This means, therefore, that it is necessary that we must, above all, stop limiting ourselves. Our destiny is to be as Christ is, and with a soul full to the brim with the Power of God, directed divinely toward his purposes, there is no limit to what He can achieve through us, except for such bodily limitations which God Himself has put upon us, and these only He knows. A true Christian should never limit the Happiness, Joy, and Spiritual Strength which he can attain by allowing the Power of God to light his life. Remember that Paul said, "I can do all things through Christ who strengthens me."[8]

"The grace of our Lord Jesus Christ be with you all. Amen." (Phillipians 4:23.)

---

[8] (Philippians 4:13) "I can do all things through Christ which strengtheneth me."

AUTHOR AND SUBJECT INDEX

INDEX OF BIBLICAL QUOTATIONS